Managing the Four Different Generations in the Workplace Effectively, Efficiently, and Successfully

DR. LARRY PRICE

Fulton Books, Inc.
Meadville, PA

First originally published by Fulton Books 2018

ISBN 978-1-63338-643-3 (Paperback)
ISBN 978-1-63338-664-8 (Hardcover)
ISBN 978-1-63338-644-0 (Digital)

Printed in the United States of America

DEDICATION

—⬦—

I want to thank my mother, father, grandmother, and grandfather who believed and instilled in me that if you have valuable information that can benefit others then it should be shared.

NOTE TO READER

The purpose of the research/book was to investigate how to manage the four different generations effectively, efficiently, and successfully in the workplace, and to ascertain which methods, theories, or activities of motivation can be utilized to enhance motivation and cohesiveness among generations when their work ethic differ. This is the first time in the history of the workplace where you have four different and unique generations coming together in the workplace. The four different generations working in the same environment in today's contemporary is a phenomenon, and trying to manage everybody could be challenging. Based on the phenomena that have been identified, a qualitative research phenomenology method was utilized for the research. The research will reveal some of the motivating theories and methods that will increase the motivation and cohesiveness among the four different generations in the workplace to support and achieve the goals of the company. It is critical to understanding the generational differences. The data collected/gathered were taken from individual participants and focus group interviews. The interviewer's questions were structured. The open-ended questions were designed to obtain detailed description information. The analyzed data form thirteen themes for creating success among the four different generations in the workplace through motivation and cohesiveness.

CONTENTS

—⊷⫘⊶—

CHAPTER 1

INTRODUCTION

This is the first time in the history of the workplace where you have four different and unique generations coming together in the workplace. Motivating these different generations appropriately could decide the success or failure of companies. Motivation can aid the different generations by getting them over the artificial hurdles and bumps in their paths put in place by management who did not understand the differences between the generations. Delcampo, Haggerty, Hanely, and Knippel (2011) stated in their book *Managing the Multi-Generational Workforce* that to create a more motivated and cohesive workplace, management must view the generational difference as a strength.

Based on academic research, *Managing the Multi-Generational Workforce* identifies several of the characteristics of the different generations. Traditionalists, born before 1945, numbered approximately seventy-five million people. The Baby Boomers, born from 1946 until 1964, number approximately eighty million people, making this group the largest population of people ever born in the United States. Generation X (Gen X) was born between 1965 and 1980, and has approximately forty-six million people. Millennials, born between 1981 and 2001, with a population of seventy-six million, show the most promise.

According to Toossi, an economist in the Office of Occupational Statistics and Employment Projections at the Bureau of Labor Statistics, the labor force of the future will be ascertained by the dynamism of the US population shift from Baby Boomers to Gen Xers and Millennials. However, the impact of the Baby Boomers on the composition and labor force will still be a key factor. With the increase in life expectancies and the financial need to supplement their retirement, some Baby Boomers will continue to work. This seems to be a motivation for them. Gravetta and Throckmorton (2007) explained the unique perspectives and experiences each generation brings to the workforce, and how generational management needs to tap into the energy of generational talent by bringing together generations with different motivational needs, perceptions, and behavior styles.

Managing the different generations to increase motivation and cohesiveness will be imperative, as the US population shifts from Baby Boomers to Gen Xers and Millennials because of the different beliefs, norms, behaviors, and expectations. In *Managing Different Generations at Work*, Marshall (2004) concluded that each generation is motivated by different factors and brings their own expectations to the workplace.

With the appropriate motivation methods and theories, managers can generate new ideas and voices that present a fresh way of thinking from the members of each of the four different generations. Two of the most powerful motivational tools are intrinsic motivation and extrinsic motivation. Jeffrey (2009) agreed that involving all employees in the development and implementation of the reward programs will encourage motivation and communication between workers and management. The companies should make appropriate rewards to the different generations an integral part of their strategy to increase motivation and cohesiveness among members of the generations.

Members from the different generations can be motivated by effective communications, active listening, taking a serious interest in the future path of a worker's career, and the importance of a work/life balance. Raghupathy (2010) agreed that for today's managers and supervisors, managing teams and individuals from the Traditionalist, Baby Boomer, Gen Xer, and Millennial generations with different skill sets, experiences, and technological proficiency can present challenging situations where management can engage these unique employees and motivate them to form a unified and cohesive team to bring resolution to problems, and increase productivity, creativity, and innovation for the company.

This is why it is critical that companies understand the different characteristics of each generation. The current projections of the labor force performed by the Bureau of Labor Statistics reveal a population and labor force that will have the characteristics of change over the next fifty years. The aging of both the population and the labor force will result in a declining growth rate of the workforce. The labor workforce aged fifty-five and older is rising at an alarming rate due to an increase in life expectancies, and decrease in fertility rates of the US population.

By the year 2020, the share of the workforce that will be held by those fifty-five years and older is projected to be approximately 24%. There will be significant numbers of older age groups (Baby Boomers) in the workforce who will be retiring, thus resulting in a loss of crucially needed talent and skills, and great amounts of institutional knowledge. The population and the workforce are projected to become more racially and ethnically diverse.

The participation rate of male workers twenty-five to fifty-four years old was 90.5% in 2005, and is projected to be 90.5% in 2010, and to decrease to 90.2% by 2050. The participation rate for women in this same age group is expected to increase from a level of 75.3% in 2005, to 75.7% in 2010, and 76.6% by 2050. Historical data shows that, as a result of many factors, the workforce participation rate of workers fifty-five years and older has increased significantly since the end of the 1980s.

How these different generations are effectively and efficiently managed will ascertain the bottom line of the company and its future in the industry. To manage these different generations effectively and efficiently, employers must apply the appropriate motivational methods and theories. Without a motivated and cohesive organization there will be no innovation, no creative processes, low productivity, and low morale. Unmotivated employees can impede productivity and retention, and damage the reputation of the company.

In *Understanding Employees is a Generational Thing*, Hall (2007) defined and discussed the characteristics of four different generations in the workplace. This article explains that the workforce in the near future with older workers more than likely will work longer for money and for mental and social stimulation. The younger workers would probably require flexible schedules for taking care of sick parents and small children. This article offers two key issues facing younger workers from the Gen X and Millennial generations in the workplace. One is the need to develop people skills that will enable them to communicate and motivate the Traditionalists and Baby Boomers by making them to want to improve their technological proficiency which will make them perform their assignments more efficiently.

In managing the different generations, increasing cohesiveness and motivation will have a profound impact on an organization's productivity and sustainability. It is very important to understand the generational differences when it comes to cohering, motivating, managing, recruiting, and retaining employees in the workplace because each generation has their own beliefs, norms, culture, and social structure. The managers and supervisors who do not investigate the different methods and strategies for managing each generation will have difficulty motivating and forming cohesive groups or teams with the different generations. Again, it is very important to understand the generational differences when it comes to recruiting, retaining, and managing new employees in the workplace because each generation has their own beliefs, norms, cultures, and social structure.

Kian, Yusoff, and Rajah (2013) stated that extrinsic and intrinsic factors are important motivational tools that can be utilized to increase motivation among the Gen Xers and Millennials. Whether it is to increase productivity or cohesiveness, these motivational methods can be successful with the Gen Xers and Millennials. Kian et al. (2013) found that Gen Xers had a positive correlation with intrinsic factors and a negative correlation with extrinsic factors, while Millennials had a positive correlation with extrinsic factors and a negative correlation with intrinsic factors.

Gen Xers are motivated by taking on challenging assignments to increase their marketability. Millennials are motivated by collaborating on organizing activities and state of the art equipment such as computers and smart phones. They depend on good teamwork with their team members (Murphy, Gibson, and Greenwood, 2010). Social media is a very important motivational factor for Millennials.

Motivation affects human behavior and performance with each generation. Each generation is motivated differently. What motivates one generation might not motivate the other generations. Saraswathi (2011) believed that motivation is the willingness to exert a high level of performance toward the goals of the organization by the efforts' ability to satisfy some individual need.

Because of the Baby Boomers' retirement, in the next five to ten years, there will be a talent war between companies to recruit and retain the best employees. When Baby Boomers retire, there will be a tremendous brain drain on companies in terms of leadership, knowledge, skill, and technique, leaving a leadership gap in upper management in corporations. In the future workforce, companies will be looking for experiences, skill sets, assets, adaptability, and flexibility. When the Baby Boomers retire in the next five to ten years, all companies will be competing for those resources.

Collis and Montgomery (2008) stated that experiences, assets, skills, and organizational cultures determine how efficiently and effectively a company performs its organizational activities in the workplace. The different generations provide the set of unique experiences and skills, and set or contribute to the organizational cultures. These organizational capabilities must be rooted in the company's procedures, processes, and culture. For example, the skill set of the Baby Boomers could complement the skill set of the Gen Xers, while the skill set of the Gen Xers could complement the skill set of the Millennials. The skill set of the Traditionalists could complement the skill set of the Baby Boomers. This should be a component of companies' strategic planning. It is critical that companies realize this, so a customized recruiting, retaining, and managing plan can be assembled for the different generations.

From a company's point of view, this awareness and knowledge of the different generations will be time and money well invested because it promotes creativity and innovation that could lead to competitive advantages and sustainability. It can strengthen motivation, thereby giving employees a sense of accomplishment and responsibility. This knowledge could have a positive impact on the organizational culture of the company which will enable employees and management to build up trust and will enable managers and supervisors to create clarity and purpose among the different generations. This can develop collaborative relationships, enhancing the company's productivity.

Do generations differ in level of work motivation, and if so, are differences in work motivation better explained by managerial level than by the generations? The focus of a study by Deal et al. (2013) stated that managerial level explains work motivation better than generation. Although the generations did differ in external work motivation, there was more difference in work motivation explained by managerial level. For example, employees at the lower managerial level had a higher level of external motivation than those at the higher managerial level.

The four basic elements of motivation are: economic incentives, passion, recognition, and vision. With these four elements of motivation, employees at the low managerial level have a main external motivation of economic incentives and recognition. The employees at the higher managerial levels are internally motivated by passion, pride, vision, and sense of accomplishment. This describes extrinsic motivation and intrinsic motivation.

To the researcher, in some cases, this would make perfect sense because at the lower level of management, one is not making much money, so to compensate, economic incentives would be the driving motivational factor. The employees at the higher levels of management are making more money, so their driving motivational factor would be passion, pride, and sense of achievement. Understanding that work motivations are connected to management level rather than generations will improve our knowledge of generational differences and motivation in the workplace.

Osterloh and Frey (2000) agreed that employees are motivated intrinsically, as well as extrinsically. Intrinsic motivation is imperative when knowledge is being transferred between generations for the company's sustainable competitive advantage. Again, intrinsic motivational factors are passion, pride, and sense of achievement.

Transformational leadership can increase motivation and cohesiveness among the four different generations in the workplace. Transformational leadership can generate motivation, cohesiveness, productivity, performance, and morale through mechanisms, characteristics, and style.

Transformational leaders can articulate a vision for the future. In transformational leadership, it is the leader who must have the self-assurance, charisma, confidence, and belief that he or she can personally make a difference and impact on employees, organizations, groups, and people (Benson, 2008). This includes people of different generations. Transformational leadership goes farther than participatory leadership, situational leadership, and transactional leadership by awareness and acceptance of the organization's purpose and mission, and by getting the employees, organizations, groups, and people to see beyond their own needs and self-interest for the betterment of all.

Transformational leadership during crisis and ethical dilemma can motivate employees, organizations, groups, and people by driving them to accomplish more than they could have imaged to solve the crisis or ethical dilemma. Transformational leadership works by obtaining every ounce of the employees' energies and drives to accomplish the mission to bring about change, and by creating a culture of motivation, cohesiveness, and ethical behavior. According to Conger (1999), the fundamental elements of transformational influence used by leaders to induce or bring about change are influencing followers by establishing a vision for a better future, inspiring followers as opposed to controlling them, leading by example through role modeling, contributing to subordinates' intellectual stimulation, enhancing meaningfulness of goals and behaviors, fulfilling followers' self-actualization needs, empowering followers through intrinsic motivation, exhibiting confidence in subordinates' abilities to attain higher levels of achievement, and enhancing collective identity.

A transformational leader should influence followers by articulating a new and clear vision. The research methodology that was utilized will be qualitative. The results, conclusions, and recommendations of the qualitative approach of the study will be provided in Chapter 5 Summary, Conclusions and Recommendations.

BACKGROUND AND PROBLEM STATEMENT

Managing the different generations is necessary in order to increase cohesiveness and motivation. The four different generations in the workplace can create challenges and conflicts for managers and supervisors who must deal with competing priorities, agenda, and values. Having these four different generations in the workplace will create conflicts and collision in the workplace.

Lancaster and Stillman (2005) believed that collisions in the workplace happened when two generations bump into each other over just about anything in terms of processes, procedures, policies, lack of cohesiveness, motivation, and the organization's culture. For example, cultures can clash when methods and work ethics differ from one generation to the next. All the generations view situations from their own generational perspectives and experiences, and therefore, those managers who do not investigate different methods and activities for managing each generation are having difficulty motivating and forming cohesiveness with the different generations. Managers and supervisors are not retaining people of the different generations because they do not know of the different motivation and cohesiveness concepts, theories, and strategies.

Each generation has unique styles, behaviors, ways of thinking, ways of communicating, and abilities. Again, it is very important to understand the generational differences when it comes to recruiting, retaining, and managing new employees in the workplace because each generation has its own beliefs, norms, cultures, and social structure. It is critical that companies realize this so that a more custom-ized recruiting, retaining, and managing plan can be assembled for the different generations.

Management that fails in investigating different motivation and cohesiveness theories, methods, and activities for managing each generation could increase the turnover rates of good and talented employees. The costs associated with high turnover are recruiting, hiring, and training new employees. With high turnover comes a decrease in productivity, efficiency, creativity, and innovation. According to Lancaster and Stillman (2005), these are the tangible and intangible costs of company turnover.

It is critical that companies realize this so that a more cus-tomized recruiting, retaining, and managing plan can be assembled for the different generations. Each generation has its own unique style, behavior, way of thinking, way of communicating, and abil-ity. Managers and supervisors have problems managing the different generations' workplace because they do not know of the different motivation and cohesiveness concepts, theories, and strategies.

The workplace function of the past was that orders given by managers and supervisors were simply just followed. There were no questions asked. An employee had to follow orders. Those days are long gone in an attempt to get things accomplished in today's work-place with the different generations. The modern generations do not respond well to this type of managerial style.

Management's style will have to change and evolve if it is to manage the modern generations in a way that increases cohesiveness and motivation. Motivating and engaging the different generations can contribute positive impacts to companies and their internal orga-nizations. The companies' managers and supervisors will need to be aware of the characteristics of each generation. This knowledge will enable managers and supervisors to better understand the people who will benefit the company by utilizing their skills and abilities to be more productive, and to establish measurable goals for themselves and their companies.

Cohesiveness, motivation, and productive work enable the employees to work individually and as a group member. Each generation has its strengths and weakness. The members of the older generations show characteristics that accommodate customer service and loyalty to a company. The younger generations have the technical savvy, skills, and knowledge, and the ability to train and tutor others to use this technology to benefit the company.

With rapid political, economic, and global climates, it is essential to consider the challenges facing a company and understand that survival will depend on its bringing together its generational workforces. Workplaces must be redefined, and organizations are being pressed to adapt to this new wave of workers infused in companies. A critical aspect of this phenomenon is not receiving sufficient research attention regarding the impact of the four different generations in the workplaces.

Again, companies today face serious challenges as they travel on a path forward through unprecedented uncertainty and economic challenges. The generational differences have noticeable practical impacts on businesses finances, such as increased incomes, sales, profit margins, and cash flow. The workplace dynamics change as its values and opinions impact the way organizations function, operate, and interact.

PURPOSE OF THE STUDY

The purpose of the study was to investigate how to manage the four different generations in order to increase cohesiveness and motivation which will lead to their effectiveness, efficiencies and success in the workplace and to ascertain which methods, theories, or activities of motivation can be utilized to enhance motivation and cohesiveness among each generation and minimize collisions and clashes among the generations when their behavior, collide and clashes among the generations and their behavior, beliefs, cultures, norms, agendas, values, priorities and work ethic differ. Data was collected from interviews and focus group and the utilization of this information is included in this research study.

Motivating and engaging the different generations can lead to new innovated products and services for the company. Managers and supervisors need to be aware of how to motivate people of different generations, and capitalize on their different strengths to increase their effectiveness, cohesiveness and motivation. The understanding of beliefs, norms, cultures, and behavior is an important tool in establishing employee motivation and cohesiveness. Knowing how to coach, motivate, and bring about cohesiveness in today's different generations in the workplace will be an important factor to an organization's success.

RESEARCH QUESTION

What are the different methods, theories, or activities of motivation that can be utilized by managers to make the four generations work together effectively and efficiently in the workplace and enhance motivational efforts among each of these generational groups? The research question for investigation is of importance as it can assist managers, supervisors, and leaders in the workplace. Dealing with the different generations will take different styles, methods, and practices.

DEFINITIONS OF TERMS

According to Locke, Spirduso, and Silverman (2007), those terms outside the field of study of readers should be defined for a clearer understanding of the research study proposal. These are terminologies or jargons that the readers would not otherwise understand.

Baby Boomers: people born from 1946 to 1964 (Shaw, 2013, p. 7).
Generation: significant shared attitudes, behaviors, conditions and events that people were exposed to as they grew up (Zemke, Raines, and Flipczak, 2013, p. 17).

Gen Xers/Generation X/Generation Xers: people born from 1965 to 1980 (Shaw, 2013, p. 7).

Gen–Y/Millennial: people born from 1981 to 2001 (Shaw, 2013, p .7).

Traditionalists/Matures/Veterans: people born before 1945 (Shaw, 2013, p. 7).

LIMITATIONS AND DELIMITATIONS OF STUDY

Limitations are the circumstances and situations that the researchers cannot control. Delimitations are the circumstances and situations that the researchers can control. External validity threats arise when experimenters draw incorrect inferences from the sample data to other persons, other settings, and past or future situations.

There could be some unavoidable problems that could limit the findings such as financial and sample size, therefore limiting the statistical data. As a Baby Boomer, my personal knowledge and subjectivity of the Baby Boomer generation could present a bias. The researcher experienced some bias in determining some of the collected data. Limitations of studies generally derive from two sources: the decisions made about how to conduct the study, and the problems that arose when implementing the study (Cone and Foster, 1993).

SIGNIFICANCE OF THE STUDY

The significance of this study is that the information gained can be utilized to assist managers and supervisors in developing a cohesive group, and would enable them to use methods, theories, and activities to enhance motivation and cohesion. This might assist organizations in becoming more motivated, cohesive, efficient, and productive.

CHAPTER 2

REVIEW OF THE LITERATURE

The literature review provided the information about the different characteristics between the four generations in the workplace. The literature also provided theories and methods that can be utilized to increase motivation and cohesiveness among the four different generations in the workplace. This is the first time in the history of the workplace where we have four different generations working together. Members of each generation are motivated differently.

The generational clash over how to accomplish the assignments and complete the missions seems to have people going in different directions. Unrealistic expectations collide with their contrasting work styles. The literature review contained information that explained why one motivation and cohesive method will not work to achieve the desired results from Traditionalists, Baby Boomers, Gen Xers, and Millennials.

The literature review provided an understanding as to why such differences in beliefs, values, norms, behaviors, social structures, and attitudes between generations exist. However, this does not mean that one generation is better than the other. Some information was provided to make managers, supervisors, and employees aware that generational shifts were occurring and offered some effective motivational methods for the four different generations in the workplace to aid in supporting and achieving the objectives of the organization. In the study of the management of the different generations to increase motivation and cohesiveness, the literature review will cover these topics: Workplace Differences Characteristics of the Four Generations; Generations in the Workplace and Impacts, Benefits; Employee's Cost of Turnover; Reasons for Turnover of Employees; Stress Across the Four Different Generations; Motivating the Four Different Generations; Transformational Leadership for Motivating and Cohesiveness for the Four Different Generations; Path—Goal Theory; Culture/Organizational Culture and Strategies for Recruitment, and; Retention of the Four Different Generations in the Workplace. There are many books and articles dealing with this phenomenon of the four different generations in the workplace from motivational and leadership aspects (Zemke et al., 2013; Shaw, 2013; McChesney, Covey, and Huling, 2012; Gordinier, 2008; Erickson 2008; Conley, 2007; White and Prywes, 2007; Marston, 2007; McClain and Romaine, 2007; Steinhorn, 2006; Twenge, 2006; Loehr and Kaye, 2011; Emmerich, 2009; Gilman, 2001; Davila, Epstein, and Shelton, 2006; Barnes, 2005; Green, 2000; Connerley and Pedersen, 2005; Hesselbein, Goldsmith, and Somerville, 2002; Lancaster and Stillman, 2005; Drucker, 2002; Wlodkowski, 1999).

WORKPLACE DIFFERENCES CHARACTERISTICS OF THE FOUR GENERATIONS

Traditionalists/Veterans/Matures (People born before 1945)

The Traditionalists were people born before 1945. This group grew up during two world wars and a nationwide economic upheaval (Shaw, 2013). This economic upheaval was known as the Great Depression. They can remember the soup lines for people needing help to feed themselves and their families. If you had a job during this period, you were considered fortunate.

The Traditionalists believe in country, honor, duty, and loyalty (Brokaw, 1998). They respected authority and believed in following orders. This is how tasks got accomplished. The subordinates would take orders from their superiors, and follow those orders to get the job accomplished. This type of thinking is from the military environment during the war era.

In civilian life, you were glad to have a job, and you would probably stay with that company until you retired. There was a feeling that the company would take care of you. People of this generation came from nuclear families with two parents. The father would go to work to make the money to support his family, while the mother would stay home and take care of the children and domestic affairs. Again, these people faced world wars and challenging economic times which made them strong and very thrifty with money. Therefore, Traditionalists may not be motivated by large salaries or fancy job titles because the majority of the traditionalists who are in today's workplace are there because of socializing or to have an income to supplement retirement.

The Traditionalists are believed to be the most amazing generation. Their depression was the Great One and their war was the Big One. The Traditionalists saved the world for democracy and freedom, and are credited with building a nation. Traditionalists are team players and community-minded people (Brokaw, 1998). Through war, suffering, economic depression, and peacekeeping, this generation kept its focus on moving forward until a great nation was formed.

Traditionalists pledged their loyalty to the companies that employed them. The companies in turn provided the Traditionalists a means to support and take care of their families and put their children through school. Their companies would provide them with a job for life, and a pension for retirement if they were fortunate to work for a good company. For the Traditionalists, they could not ask their companies for more.

Today, Traditionalists feel underappreciated and overlooked after all their accomplishments and capabilities. Also, we must not overlook that the greatest generation gave birth to the Baby Boomers that went on to establish their own presence. Companies must not forget that each generation has its own culture, social structure, behavior, and priorities (Loehr and Kaye, 2011).

Baby Boomers (1946–1964)

The Baby Boomers are children of the Traditionalists who were born after World War II ended. The Baby Boomers had more opportunities than their parents in terms of education and political freedom. This is why this generation was more politically active during the sixties and seventies than some of their parents. This generation wanted to change the world for the better (Steinhorn, 2006). The Baby Boomers who were born between 1946 and 1964 were raised after two world wars, and the country had come out of an economic upheaval (Shaw, 2013).

The Baby Boomers are known for their work ethic. The Baby Boomers will work until the job is completed. The Baby Boomers believe that you are defined by your job. The Baby Boomers had to work hard because of the fierce competition from other Baby Boomers. There were approximately seventy-seven to eighty million Baby Boomers all competing for the same jobs.

Visibility in front of the boss or the company hierarchy is very important for Baby Boomers. The Baby Boomers prefer formal meetings and annual performance reviews. Financial security, retirement benefits, and job stability are all important to the Baby Boomers.

Baby Boomers are competitive people. This was because of the large population of people all coming of age at nearly the same time. The result was that Baby Boomers felt that younger and less experienced workers must pay their dues before getting good jobs with a title and an office with a window.

Baby Boomers are motivated by competitive salaries and opportunities for growth, development, and career advancement. The Baby Boomers were *save the world* revolutionaries of the sixties and seventies. They were responsible for the Consciousness Movement of the country. The Baby Boomers' activism led to Civil Rights, the Vietnam War, Campus Unrest, Women's Rights, and Rock and Roll

(Steinhorn, 2006). The country developed a sense of fair play for all of its citizens.

Gen Xers/Generation X/Generation Xers (1965–1980)

The Generation Xers were brought up during the mid-sixties to 1980. During this time, there was protesting for equal rights, equality, and against the Vietnam War (Gordinier, 2008). There was the Watergate incident that caused a president to resign, partly because he was not honest with the American people and Congress. Generation Xers saw their parents lose jobs and livelihoods, as the migration of jobs began heading south to Mexico and overseas.

Generation Xers started to distrust their government and corporate America. They lacked confidence in their leaders and heroes. Generation Xers believed that they had to change jobs often to build up their skills and experiences to make them more flexible in the job market (Gordinier, 2008). They have little loyalty to companies.

Gen Xers are technologically proficient, independent, and creative thinkers who are unimpressed with authority. Generation Xers want to be compensated adequately for their performances. Generation Xers grew up smart and savvy but distant and isolated because their parents were divorced or career driven. According to the US Census Statistics, in 1971 the divorce rate was 50% higher than a decade earlier. Because both parents were working, dual income households became normal (Stevenson and Wolfers, 2007).

The Generation Xers want to make their marriage work and be there for their children. The Gen Xers are entrepreneurial and extremely individualistic. The government and big businesses do not mean much to them. They want to save the neighborhood but not the universe. The Generation Xers feel misunderstood by the other generations. They do not trust the major institutions because these institutions failed their parents and them during their adolescent years (Zemke et al., 2013).

Millennials/Generation Y (1981–2001)

Millennials were born between 1981 and 2001, and were raised during the high technology decades (Shaw, 2013). They have experienced microwaves, computers, ATMs, wireless phones, wireless computers, twenty-four hours of cable television news, and the superhighway of information internet. Everything was instantaneous; just push a button or go to your computer key board and click. There are approximately 100 million Millennials. This is the largest generation since the Baby Boomers, and the most promising. The Millennials are multitaskers, optimistic, technologically proficient, adaptable, and impatient (Erickson, 2008).

They are very impatient especially when it comes to salary increases and promotions. Millennials tend to want everything now. Millennials were born into diversity. They were brought up in a diverse environment.

Every generation is unique and brings something new and innovative to the company, whether it is a new concept or building on an existing concept that will improve the bottom line of the company. These generations can increase market share and create value to the company. Millennials feel the need to schedule everything on their smart phones and computers. Millennials are cooperative team players and masters of social media. They have great confidence in themselves, high expectations for themselves, and could be America's next great generation (Twenge, 2006).

In the future, all companies should develop generational strategies for employee training, human resources, management, organizational development, recruitment, and retention. Generational sensitivity is a phase that all companies should be familiar with in the future. Each generation has its own beliefs, norms, values, styles, and ways of thinking.

Table 1

Generational Difference Characteristics

Traditionalists	Baby Boomers	Generation Xers	Millennials
Follow orders	Workaholic	Technologically proficient	Multitaskers
Respect authority	Very competitive	Independence	Optimistic
Conformity	Embrace political freedom	Unimpressed with authority	Technologically proficient
Hierarchy	Loyalty to company	No loyalty to company	Adaptable
Duty and country	Build a career	Great candidates for leadership position	Impatient
Loyal to employers	Salary	Build portable career	Demand diversity
Sacrifice	Special Recognition	Job change is necessary	Social group
Dedication	Office with View	No micro-management	Requires frequent feedback on performance
Build a Legacy	Prestigious Titles	A balanced work life	Can be loyal to an organization
A job well done			Build parallel careers

Generations in the Workplace and Impacts

In the workplace, we have representation of all the generations. We have the Traditionalists born before 1945, Baby Boomers born between 1946 and 1964, Gen Xers born between 1965 and 1980, and Generation Y/Millennials born between 1981 and 2001 (Shaw, 2013). These four generations in the workplace have different expectations pertaining to attitudes, behaviors, mentality, motivations, norms, and values. If all managers and supervisors in the workplace had an understanding of these generational differences, it would benefit the management in providing responses to workplace situations with increased knowledge of how to deal with the different generations.

The Traditionalists and Baby Boomers will remain in the workforce because of advances in medicine. People now are healthier as they age. An economic factor would be the increase in the Social Security eligibility age. This provides the incentives for people to stay in the workforce. Based on the US Bureau of Labor Statistics's figures, because of such factors, the number of people in the labor force aged sixty-five and older is expected to grow approximately ten times faster than the total labor force (U.S. Bureau of Labor Statistics, n.d.)

Some of the generational impacts would be ineffective communication that will lead to misunderstandings and decreased recruitment and employee retention. The motivational methods and theories that are being utilized in the workplace could be ineffective because of generational differences. The decrease in productivity, innovation, creativity, teamwork, and expectations would be a serious consequence of not understanding the generational differences. High turnover rates, increased tangible costs, high complaints and grievances, and low morale in the workplaces are all results of not understanding generational differences.

In future workforces, companies will be looking for experiences, skill sets, assets, adaptability, and flexibility capabilities. When the Baby Boomers retire in the next five to ten years, all companies will be competing for those resources. Collis and Montgomery (2008) asserted that experiences, assets, skills, and organizational cultures determine how efficiently and effectively a company performs its organizations' activities.

The different generations provide unique experiences, skill sets, and talents that contribute to the organizational cultures. These organizational capabilities must be rooted in the company's procedures, process, and culture. For example, the skill set of the Traditionalists could complement the Baby Boomers skill set, which could complement the skill set of the Generation Xers. The skill set of the Gen Xers could complement the skill set of the Millennials. This should be a component of an organization's strategic planning.

In 2007, Traditionalists made up eight percent of the workplace, while Baby Boomers made up 46%, Gen Xers 23%, and Millennials 23%. The projected composition of the workplace in 2015 is Traditionalists three percent, Baby Boomers 41%, Gen Xers 20%, and Millennials 37%. Millennials could be the generation to save us all because of their characteristics (Stein, 2013).

According to the US Department of Labor, the number of people in the labor force aged fifty-five to sixty-four is expected to grow by 33% between 2008 and 2018, and the number of people aged sixty-five and older is projected to grow by 78%. The numbers of forty-five to fifty-four year olds, and thirty-five to forty-four year olds are expected to fall, as Baby Boomers age and shift into older groups. The total labor force is expected to average approximately eight percent during the projection's decade (U.S. Bureau of Labor Statistics, n.d.).

According to Delta Airlines, "by 2020, nearly half our employees and customers will be millennials, and we have been spending a lot of time learning how to reach out to the emerging generation."(Sky Delta Magazine June 2017 Edition, page 11/June 2017 Issue Digital Edition, page 11) Delta Airlines is getting ahead of the curve now which will be a huge advantage for their company.

How these generations think differently about economic, political, and social influences can affect their performances, cooperations, and support. The structure of the family, education, work ethic, and values can affect performances. Each generation's leadership style, communication style, motivational style, inspirational style, and interactions with colleagues would be different. The selective approach to feedback and view toward the company will be seen through each generation's perspectives.

Each generation will have different views on work, personal life, rewards, financial behaviors, and expectations and relationships with technology will be different which will in turn affect performances and cooperations. The generations' social influences could have been major events such as music from Benny Goodman, Glen Miller, Elvis Presley, Frank Sinatra, Sammy Davis Jr., The Beatles, James Brown, Sam Cooke, Rolling Stones, Michael Jackson, Brittany Spears, or Justin Timberlake. The generations' political influences would be World War I, World II, Prime Minister Churchill, President Roosevelt, military services, President Harry Truman, President John F. Kennedy, Dr. Martin Luther King Jr, the Cold War, Watergate, the Iran Contra Affair, or the Monica Lewinsky incident. The generations' economic influences would have been major financial scandals such as Enron, WorldCom, and Global Crossing that wrecked the economy.

One significant reason why Gen Xers view corporations with skepticism is because their parents may have lost their jobs and security. These same corporations almost put this country in a depression. The people demanded action from Congress and the Senate, asking that laws be passed to prevent this from happening in the future. The Enron Scandal was the major motivator behind the Public Company Accounting Reform and Investor Protection Act of 2002, better known as Sarbanes-Oxley or SOX (Bainbridge, 2007). However, the major decisions of the company are being made by the Baby Boomer generation with some inputs from the Traditionalist generation.

The Traditionalist generation grew up during an economic upheaval. This affects the research and development, design, products, marketing, sales, manufacturing, financing, human resources, quality, and risk taking of the company. The Traditionalist generation's thinking is that if the company is doing alright, why take dangerous and unnecessary risks? If you manufacture a good product, then people will buy it.

The Baby Boomers feel that more is needed than just manufacturing a good product. They need to keep inventing and modifying the product to increase market shares and increase sales and profit margins. The Baby Boomers do not mind working late. Baby

Boomers often clash with Traditionalists over concepts, methods, and direction of the company.

To understand how Boomers have changed America, think back to the 1950s, but without the nostalgia. Women were kept at home, minorities were denied their dignity, homosexuality was a crime, and anyone who marched to a different drummer was labeled un-American and viewed as a threat. Today, we live in a far more open, inclusive, tolerant, and equal America than at any other time in our history. And that is because the Baby Boomers from the sixties onward have fought a great cultural war to free America from its prejudices, inequalities, and fear (Steinhorn and Leonard, 2006).

The Traditionalist generation always seems to take a conservative approach, or want the company to move in a more conservative and safe direction. With fierce competition from major competitors, this approach could be a disaster. But Traditionalists are gradually being phased out of the major decision-making capacity.

The Gen Xers and the Millennials have little to no power at the present time, however, their time will come. The Gen Xers are resourceful and independent thinkers because they grew up in two recessions and watched their parents lose their jobs. A new terminology was born, and it was called corporate downsizing. It did not take the Gen Xers long to realize that there was no job security.

Gen Xers and Millennials believe in career security. To survive during the Gen Xers' generation, one had to be resourceful, think outside of the box, and gain skills and experiences in order to be flexible. Also, one has to be creative in their reasoning and thinking. The Gen Xers do not want to work late. "In reality, Generation X is diligent, innovative, enterprising, wise, poetic, and downright visionary, but its status as the smaller, snarkier, sandwiched-in-the-middle demographic has led to its gradual marginalization on the main stage" (Gordinier, 2008, p. 9).

The Millennials are multitaskers, very capable of doing more than one activity at a time. In the workplace, Millennials seem to want everything now. It could be anything from salary increases to promotions to acknowledgment for a job well done, but they want it immediately. In other words, the Millennials want immediate gratification.

The Millennials grew up during the Desert Storm Conflict in the Middle East. It is very difficult to retain Millennials in a company. Millennials feel that any company would want their skills and abilities.

You have recently entered the workforce. In many ways, you are part of the most plugged-in group the world has seen: you are a natural networker on the job, you are on Facebook, and you get text messages and e-mails anywhere and everywhere. But despite these many connections, you are on a different page than a lot of your coworkers, many of whom were raised in a different time and just do not seem to get it. They often misunderstand you, and you have been called impatient, narcissistic, and entitled. What about your positive qualities, your fresh perspective, your motivation, your willingness to take risks, and so many others (Erickson, 2008)?

Another reason for the way the Millennials behave is that they grew up in nontraditional families in a time with a record high divorce rate. Many Millennials had both fathers and mothers work, and also take part in raising their children. Millennials' parents were more focused on their children's education and extracurricular activities. This gives the Millennials a strong sense of confidence and the belief that they can achieve anything.

In the workplace, at one point or another, there will be clashes because of the different periods of time these generations grew up in which helped shape their beliefs, values, and cultures. What companies must do for the benefit of the company and its employees is to find a way for all of these generations to mesh together for maximum efficiency. This will lead to high productivity for the company, which will equate to increased market share and increased sales, and this will translate to increased profit margins for the company.

The age differences coupled with the differences in beliefs, norms, and values will eventually lead to clashes between the generations. A generational design impact can be employed in two ways. First, a company should put together good generational fits on an assignment or a project. Something that is overlooked between the generations is the style in which the generations react to business situations and their proactive style to the situation. An organization will get quicker responses from the Generation Xers and the Millennial generations, which are good for the company, as long as they are provided advice and guidance from the Baby Boomers and Traditionalists.

Generation Xers and Millennial generations believe in freelancing, working where they can obtain the most money. The different generations offer the company many choices in style, function, and performance. The Gen Xers and Millennials distrust companies because of what had happened to their parents in the workplace. The different generations working together can be a power force in the workplace. They do not have to agree with everything that each generation believes as long as there is mutual respect and trust.

Secondly, companies should use what the author calls *design generations* which is placing a member of each generation on the same assignment or project. This unique combination could help bring the generations together to work on common objectives and goals for the company. When generational clashes get in the way of completing an assignment or project, companies should apply some of the concepts and techniques from books and training classes on the different generations. It will not be easy to bridge the generational gaps, but with training, awareness, skill, motivation, and cohesiveness methods, it can be done to the benefit of organizations.

Benefits

The economic and social benefits of understanding the four different generations in the workplaces are low turnover rate, reduced tangible costs, increased intangible costs, less complaints and grievances, increased productivity, increased teamwork, and positive perceptions of equity, fairness, and respect. The companies' managers and supervisors' knowledge and awareness of the generational differences and similarities can lower the turnover rate and reduce the tangible costs such as hiring, recruitment, retention, and training. There are intangible costs in terms of high morale and comradery in the company.

Understanding the generational differences will create more effective communication and reduce conflicts and misunderstanding in the workplace. There will be attitude improvements among the generations. Development of effective motivational methods for each generation will drive expectations, productivity, and teamwork. The managers and supervisors will view generational differences as a valuable strength instead of a weakness and will create a cohesive workplace (Delcampo et al., 2011).

Improved communication and collaboration between the different generations will drive the organization to achieve the objectives of the company. By learning what motivates employees from the different generations and communicating a clear challenging mission, managers will motivate the employees (Bates, 2008). With each generation working together collectively, there would be distinction between a good idea and a bad idea. A review process and rational decision process can be established. The ideas from the concept stage can be moved quickly to the working model stage. If the idea works, then further testing is performed.

Each member of the different generations must have the respect, freedom, and empowerment to explore and utilize all of their creative capability in the workplace. Research and Development's budget will be utilized more effectively and efficiently because of the motivation and cohesiveness of the different generations. Many ideas will be generated and developed because of all the talent among the generations which can lead to reaching beyond existing demand by achieving value innovation for the organization. The desired results would be the demand for new markets that could achieve sustainability for the company (Kim and Mauborgne, 2004). This is utilizing a Blue Ocean strategy.

Gen Xers and Millennials believe in the utilization of social media. These outlets provide free advertisement and publicity to their companies. The utilization of social media will increase an organization's customer base and satisfaction. The rapid response to customers' questions and needs will aid in managing customers' expectations.

Social media is playing an important role in business today and can impact organizational performance. The role that the social media plays in today's business can impact organizational performances. In the beginning, members of upper management saw social media as a distraction among the employees, especially among the young employees. They had not realized the impact and value of social media.

Social media impacts on organizational performance are driving business objectives, creating opportunities, and solving issues in the workplace. Almost everybody has access to Twitter, Facebook, LinkedIn, YouTube, and Pinterest. For example, Millennials that were born between 1982 and 2000, were raised during the high technology decades. There were microwaves, computers, ATMs, wireless phones, wireless computers, twenty-four hours of cable television news, and the internet. Everything was instantaneous.

There are approximately 100 million Millennials. This is the largest generation since the Baby Boomers, and the most promising. Millennials are multitaskers, optimistic, technologically proficient, and adaptable. The millennial generation is the most plugged-in generation.

The Millennial generation is a natural networker on the job. They are on Facebook, Twitter, and Pinterest, and get text messages and e-mails anywhere and everywhere. They are in constant contact with the organizations and the customers. This is not saying that the other generations do not utilize social media, but Millenials do it more effectively. This has become imperative for survival in an organization.

Constantly being informed about news in the organization and your need and expectations can increase the bottom line of the company such as income, sales, and profits. Most companies have added social media to their business strategies to leverage its utilization in the workplace. With social media in the workplace, there are advancements in collaboration and communication which lead to satisfied customers and employees that contribute to the bottom line of the company.

Collaboration and communication are the two primary benefits of social media. Social media enhances the social relationship among employees and customers. Employees who have access to limitless communication can impact the outcome of sales negotiations by constantly providing information to the customers' questions in a rapid time frame. Social media encourages employees' collaboration. One reason could be that because of the transparency of social media everybody wants to seem helpful and supportive on a majority of the projects. These social media networks can aid in helping ascertain the company's target audiences and their demographics, and lead to a better understanding of the customer's needs and expectations.

Then, there is what is called social integration in which sharing information has become a necessity. The employees will share almost anything that they feel passionate about. Social media networks are platforms for disseminating this information. The more social media network followers the better it is for a company in terms of sales and profits. It is interesting to note that in surveying 1,700 CEOs, 71% rate their employees as their most important source of sustained economic value (The IBM 2012 CEO Study; 2012 Social Media Marketing Industry Report). Some other interesting facts are: a) 94% of all businesses with a marketing department used social media as part of their marketing platform; b) almost 60% of the marketers are devoting the equivalent of a full workday to social media marketing development and maintenance; c) 43% of people aged twenty to twenty-nine spend more than ten hours a week on social media sites; d) 85% of all businesses that have a dedicated social media platform as part of their marketing strategy reported an increase in their market exposure; e) 58% of businesses that have used social media marketing for over three years reported an increase in sales over the period; f) more than 200 million mobile workers will be using mobile business apps in 2013, and; g) 60% of North Americans currently use their smartphones for work (Pietas Mobile Workforce Report, June 2013).

The four different generations working together can enhance productivity and creativity. The employees will have opportunities to produce more input and output. The generations working together can discover defects and make corrections, and can see their contributions to the success of the company as a feel good motivational factor. The motivation and cohesiveness among the different generations will lead to social interaction and some friendships. As motivation and cohesiveness increase so will participation, focus, and accomplishments.

Different generations understanding each other and working together can also increase conformity. However, too much conformity can have the opposite effect. The conflicts can be manageable and kept to a minimum. The generations working together will increase innovation. The company will produce new products and services for existing customers and will attract new customers. With this type of success, the employees' motivation and cohesiveness will be improved.

The synergy of different generations working together will increase motivation and cohesiveness, thereby, leading the company to gain a competitive advantage. The company sales, income, revenue, and profits will increase. Based on President George W. Bush's autobiography, he learned lessons from Roosevelt and Reagan that contributed to his leadership and these two people were not from his generation (Bush, 2010).

Employees' Cost of Turnover

The cost of high employee turnover can lead to increased tangible costs, decreased intangible cost, more complaints, more grievances, decreased productivity, decreased teamwork, and negative perceptions of equity, fairness, and respect. "Every industry is reporting higher turnover, the cost of which includes tangible expenses" (Lancaster and Stillman, 2005, p. 7). A company's managers and supervisors' lack of knowledge and awareness of generational differences can increase the turnover rate, and increase the tangible costs such as hiring, recruitment, retention, and training. The cost to a business to replace an upset employee is approximately 2.5 times his or her annual salary (Zemke et al., 2013). This means a decrease in employee recruitment and employee retention.

There are intangible costs to not understanding generational differences such as low morale and comradeship in the company. There will be more ineffective communication and more conflicts and misunderstandings in the workplace. There will be no improvement in the attitude among the different generations. The same antiquated and ineffective motivational methods will continue to be utilized in organizations, and this will drive down expectations, productivity, and teamwork. If companies keep using the same methods, they are going to get the same results.

Reasons for Turnover of Employees

Some reasons for turnover of employees are low motivation, lack of cohesiveness, low performance, lack of recognition, and not being aware of the different generations' characteristics. The managers and supervisors who say that they do not have the time to deal with the tension among the different generations will be caught in a perpetual turnover mode. By telling employees from the Millennial generation to be patient and understanding and that their time will eventually come, organizations will see an increase of turnover in the company from that group.

Millennials are not motivated by feelings of duty or working hard but by being singled out and recognized (Twenge, 2006). Millennials are not patient but impatient. They want that promotion and salary increase now. According to Twenge (2006), 60% of employers say that their workplaces suffer from tension among the generations. Motivational issues, cohesiveness issues, and tension between the four generations can escalate when managers and supervisors impetuously attempt to deal with each generation the same way.

"Job Openings and Labor *Turnover* Summary, March 11, 2014, in 2013 Annual Levels and Rates, the annual Total Separations/*Turnover* rose 51.8 million (38.0 percent of employment) and the annual quits increased to 27.6 million (20.3 percent of employment). Total separations include quits, layoffs and discharge, and other separations. Total Separations is referred to as Turnover. Quits are generally voluntary separations initiated by employee. Therefore, the quits rate can serve as a measure of workers' willingness or ability to leave job. Layoffs and discharges are involuntary separations initiated by the employer" (Bureau of Labor Statistics).

> "There were 4.0 million job openings on the last business day of January, little changed from December, the U.S. Bureau of Labor Statistics reported today. The hires rate (3.3 percent) and separations rate (3.2 percent) were little changed in January. This release includes estimates of the number and rate of job openings, hires and separations for the nonfarm sector by industry and by geographic region. The annual levels for hires and quits increased in 2013" (Bureau of Labor Statistics, n.d.).

When different generations reluctantly attempt to work with each other this could lead to emotional confusion, conflicts, misunderstanding, and miscommunication which will cause the organization and company to suffer. According to Kroll (2014), when it comes to building a superstar talent pool, hiring does not mean anything if the company cannot persuade employees to stay. By 2020, 15.7 million new project management jobs will be added around the world (Project Management Talent Gap Report, 2014).

Stress Across the Four Different Generations

All generations experience stress and its physical and emotional effects. However, there are strong contrasts between the four different generations on the causes, symptoms, and ideas for managing that stress. The Traditionalists have the lowest stress levels, and Gen Xers have the highest stress levels. The commonality between the different generations is financial concerns.

Baby Boomers, Gen Xers, and Millennials were likely to say that money is a main source of stress. The Traditionalists were likely to say the economy. Being on a fixed income, Traditionalists are concerned about inflation and taxes. Traditionalists report an average stress level of 4.4 on a 10-point scale. This is lower than the nationally reported average of 5.4. However, Traditionalists feel that a healthy level of stress would be 3.4.

Gen Xers report an average stress level of 5.8, but they feel that a healthy level of stress would be a 3.8. Sixty-nine percent of Traditionalists reported that the economy is the main source of their stress. The Traditionalists are most likely to say that their stress levels have decreased over the past five years (46% vs. 25% of the general population).

Traditionalists are doing more to manage their stress compared to Baby Boomers, Gen Xers, and Millennials. Traditionalists are at 70%, Baby Boomers at 53%, Gen Xers at 52%, and Millennials at 50%. It is reported that Gen Xers have the highest average levels of stress of any generation. Fifty-two percent of Gen Xers feel that they are doing enough to manage their stress in 2010, compared to 48% in 2009, and 45% in 2008. During the same time period, the trends show that Gen Xers reported that their stress levels were falling from an average of 6.5 on a 10-point scale in 2008, to a 5.8 in 2010.

Gen Xers are more likely to report experiencing stress related physical and emotional effects such as irritability, anger, fatigue, appetite changes, and headaches. Fifty-six percent of Gen Xers reported that they were irritable and angry because of stress compared to 30% of Traditionalists, 47% of Baby Boomers, and 43% of Millennials. Forty-seven percent of Gen Xers reported that they experienced fatigue because of stress compared to 34% of Traditionalists, 44% of Baby Boomer, and 37% of Millennials. Forty-six percent of Gen Xers reported that they had headaches because of stress compared to 22% of Traditionalists, 35% of Baby Boomers, and 36% of Millennials. Twenty-seven percent of Millennials reported a change in appetite because of stress compared to 21% of Baby Boomers, 22% of Gen Xers, and seven percent of Traditionalists.

Stress Over the Past Five Years

Fifty-one percent of Gen Xers reported that their stress increased over the past five years compared to the Millennials at 50%, Baby Boomers at 45%, and Traditionalists at 24%. Thirty-four percent of Millennials reported that their stress stayed the same over the past five years compared to Traditionalists at 31%, Gen Xers at 31%, and Baby Boomers at 28%. Forty-six percent of Traditionalists reported that their stress levels had decreased over the past five years compared to Baby Boomers 26%, Gen Xers 18%, and Millennials 16%.

Causing Stress

Money is a cause of stress for all generations. People at different stages of life have different financial and job related concerns. Eighty-five percent of Millennials reported that money was a major source of their stress compared to 76% of Baby Boomers and 75% of Gen Xers. Sixty-two percent of Traditionalists report money and job stability as major sources of stress. Fifty-nine percent of Gen Xers reported that housing costs caused stress compared to 53% of Baby Boomers and 39% of Traditionalists. Seventy-five percent of Millennials reported that work related factors were major sources of their stress compared to 71% in 2009, and 66% in 2008. Fifty-nine percent of Traditionalists reported that health problems affecting their families were a major source of stress compared to 50% of Baby Boomers, 44% of Millennials, and 39% of Gen Xers. Fifty-seven percent of Traditionalists and Baby Boomers reported that personal health concerns were a source of stress compared to 48% of the Millennials and 44% of Gen Xers.

Generations Deal with Stress

How do the different generations deal with stress? Each generation deals with stress differently. Sixty-one percent of Millennials reported that they deal with stress by listening to music compared to 49% of Gen Xers, 46% percent of Baby Boomers, and 38% of Traditionalists. Forty-eight percent of Gen Xers and Traditionalists reported that they deal with stress by exercising and walking compared to 47% of Baby Boomers and 49% of Millennials. Fifty-two percent of the Millennials reported that they deal with stress by spending time with their family and friends compared to 47% of Baby Boomers, 44% of Traditionalist, and 41% percent of Gen Xers.

Fifty-six percent of Traditionalists deal with stress by reading compared to 45% of Baby Boomers and Gen Xers, and 40% of Millennials. Thirty-two percent of Traditionalists and Millennials deal with stress by doing a hobby compared to 31% Gen Xers and Baby Boomers. Forty-three percent of Gen Xers deal with stress by watching television two hours per day compared to 38% of Baby Boomers, 35% of Traditionalists, and 34% of Millennials. Forty-four percent of Traditionalists reported that they deal with stress by praying compared to 40% of Baby Boomers, 34% of Millennials, and 29% of Gen Xers (American Psychological Association, Stress and Generation, 2010).

Motivating the Four Different Generations

McGregor's Theory and Maslow's Hierarchy of Needs

Without a motivated and cohesive organization, there will be no innovation and creative process in that organization. Without a motivated and cohesive organization, implementation of guidelines, processes, policies, and procedures would be very difficult. Unmotivated employees can impede innovation. The behavior of unmotivated employees can suffocate innovation.

An organization's strategies for motivation can be based on McGregor's Theory and the Maslow's Hierarchy of Needs. In dealing with the different generations in the workplace, there should be a blending of both models to motivate and increase cohesiveness.

McGregor's Theory believed that all employees fit in a specific group. Theory X is that employees need to be watched every second of the day (White and Prywes, 2007). The employees avoid accepting responsibility and want to be supervised, but not to the point of being micromanaged. Millennials want constant feedback on how they are doing and if they are going in the right direction.

Theory Y is that employees are willing to work without supervision (White and Prywes, 2007). The employees accept responsibility and want to achieve. This theory would work with the Traditionalist and Baby Boomer generations. The Gen Xers will be looking for responsibility that would lead to status and prestige.

Maslow's Hierarchy of Needs is represented as a pyramid with the basic needs, such as biological and physiological at the bottom and the esteem and self-actualization at the top. The biological and physiological needs are air, food, drink, shelter, warmth, sleep, and other needs. The next level up is safety need which is fundamental needs pertaining to safety and peace of mind such as: protection from the elements, security, order, law, limits, and stability (Maslow, 1943). The belonging and love needs in terms of work group, family, friendship, and affection are a part of the human equation. The esteem needs are self-esteem, achievement, mastery, independence, status, dominance, confidence, respect of others, respect by others, and managerial responsibility.

At the top of the Maslow Hierarchy of Needs Pyramid is self-actualization. The self-actualization needs are realizing personal potential, self-fulfillment, seeking personal growth, lack of prejudice, morality, creativity, problem-solving, acceptance of facts, and peak experiences. There is not one need that the different generations would disagree with, nor would they disagree with the order of levels. Maslow believed that each human being has basic physiological needs, however, human beings focus in the direction of fulfilling our lowest level needs, then move to the next (Conley, 2007). Maslow (2011) stated that self-actualization is the desire for self-fulfillment. This is everything that an individual is capable of becoming.

Table 2

McGregor's Theories

Theory X	Theory Y
Lazy	Hardworking
Avoid responsibility	Honorable/accept responsibility
Motivated through fear, intimidation and control	Motivated through respect, involvement and delegation

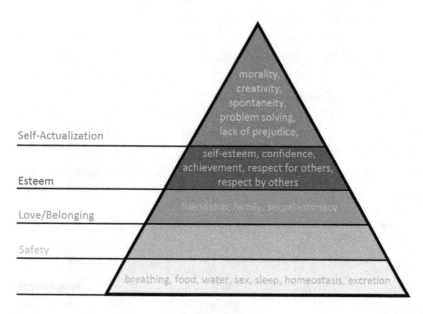

Figure 1. Maslow's Hierarchy of Needs

Alderfer's ERG Theory

Alderfer's ERG Theory reduces Maslow's Hierarchy from five needs to three. Existence would match up to Maslow's safety and physiological needs, the basic necessities. Relatedness would match up with Maslow's belongingness need, the aspiration for people to maintain interpersonal relationships. This is self–development, personal growth, and advancement. Growth would match up with Maslow's esteem and self-actualization needs (Alderfer, 1972).

Traditionalists would be motivated by the Alderfer's ERG Theory. Managers and supervisors must understand that employees from the different generations have various needs that must be satisfied. It is up to the managers and supervisors to ascertain these needs. One can just simply ask them, and they will tell you.

McClelland's Learned Needs Theory

McClelland's Learned Needs Theory states that people are motivated by the needs of affiliation, achievement, and power. Affiliation is to be liked and accepted. Achievement is to accomplish challenging assignment and goals (McClelland, 1965). Power is the ability to influence others. The Gen Xers would accept this theory because of their desire for achievement and power. If managers and supervisors do not concentrate on the needs of the employees from the different generations, then the employees will not be effectively motivated.

Herzberg's Two-Factor Theory of Motivation

Herzberg's Two-Factor Theory of Motivation states that there are some job factors that result in satisfaction, and other job factors that prevent dissatisfaction. Herzberg classified these job factors as hygiene factors and motivational agents (Mulcahy, 2002). Hygiene factors are job factors that are critical to motivation in the workplace, also called dissatisfiers as they are required to avoid dissatisfaction.

The hygiene factors symbolize physiological needs. Hygiene factors include pay, fringe benefits, physical working conditions, status, interpersonal relations, and job security.

Motivational factors yield positive satisfaction. These factors are inherent to work. These factors motivate the employees for performance. The motivational factors are recognition, sense of achievement, growth, and promotional opportunities (Mulcahy, 2002).

Intrinsic Motivation

Intrinsic motivation is defined as behavior that produces internal rewards such as pride, feelings of a job well done, and sense of achievement. The motivation to begin the behavior commences with an individual's internal need for an intrinsic reward. Intrinsic motivation occurs when an individual acts without any external reward initiative, desire, or involvement (Coon and Mitterer, 2010). Intrinsic motivation is an important tool to be utilized for motivating people to work together in a cohesive manner to support the organizational objectives of a company.

Some people perform specific activities for satisfaction and enjoyment to reinforce their certain needs (Brown, 2007). There are factors that can increase intrinsic motivation that managers and supervisors can utilize to motivate employees from the different generations in the workplace. When people are given challenging assignments that have meaning and purpose to the organization, they become motivated by their self-esteem. This is one of the levels on Maslow Hierarchy of Needs Pyramid. Sensory curiosity can motivate people by appealing to something that attracts their attention as a special and unique assignment or project. This is called cognitive curiosity.

Giving employees control over themselves and their environment and autonomy in deciding how to meet an objective can be a motivating factor. This could apply to McGregor's Theory Y which is that people want to work but not be micromanaged. Cooperation and competition can increase intrinsic motivation in situations where people enjoy helping each other and when they can compare their own performance without malice toward others. People benefit from the satisfaction of having their accomplishment recognized by associates and colleagues. This will increase their internal motivation.

What event determines whether an intrinsic motivation is to be facilitated or dismissed is important because this could affect motivation for that activity (Horn, 2008). Researchers have discovered that unnecessary rewards could carry hidden costs. For example, offering an extrinsic (external) reward for an already intrinsically rewarding activity can make the activity less intrinsically rewarding. This phenomenon is called the overjustification effect. People's intrinsic rewards from assignments provide sufficient justification for their motivation (Griggs, 2010). If people think that they are being bribed into doing an assignment or activity, then it becomes meaningless (Myers, 2005).

Extrinsic Motivation

Extrinsic motivation deals with biological, emotional, social, and cognitive forces that stimulate behavior. Extrinsic rewards are the tangible rewards given by people in authority to improve and promote motivation in getting the assignment completed. These extrinsic rewards are external to the actual work itself, and other people control their size and whether or not these rewards will be given to the person.

Extrinsic rewards are external rewards that are utilized for motivation such as trophies, salary, praise, gifts, promotions, status, and fancy offices. Extrinsic rewards played a critical role in earlier eras when the work was repetitive and bureaucratic, and when complying with regulations and procedures were of primary importance. During that time period, there were few intrinsic rewards that were offered, so the extrinsic rewards were often the only tool available to companies. However, extrinsic rewards still remain significant to employees (Straker, 2010).

Salary is an important consideration for most workers in accepting and staying with companies. In today's workplace, employees are expected and asked to self-manage to a degree by utilizing their talent and experiences to direct their work activities to achieve organizational objectives and purposes. With the four different generations motivated to work together in a cohesive manner to support the organizational objectives and purposes, employees provide added value in terms of innovating, creating, problem-solving, and improving to meet the situations they encounter to meet the customer's expectations. Companies should motivate the employees of different generations with a reward program based on their needs and expectations. Extrinsic rewards would be a good way to motivate the Millennials. The Millennials are not motivated by feelings of duty or working hard but by being singled out and recognized (Twenge, 2006).

Equity Theory

The equity Theory states that employees will be motivated when they expect and perceive that the company is treating them fairly in relation to others. The equity theory stresses the critical importance of the perceptions of being fairly treated. For example, in 2007, the average CEO made 364 times more than the average employee (Trend, 2007). A majority of the people believed that CEO pay is too high and unfair. Some companies like Aflac, a Georgia insurance company, are keeping their CEO salaries in check by having a policy that allows the investors to vote on CEO compensation packages (Lublin, 2007).

The components of the equity theory are inputs, outcomes, and referents. The inputs are the works that are contributed by the employees to the company. The inputs are considered education, training, experiences, effort, knowledge, and the number of hours worked. The outputs are what the workers receive in exchange for their contributions to the company. The outputs are considered salaries, health/medical benefits, status, job titles, and assignments. Referents in the equity theory are others with whom employees compare themselves to ascertain if they are being treated equally. Employees choose to compare themselves to the employees who hold the same or similar job functions (Kuli, 1992).

The comparison of outcomes to inputs is called the outcome/input ratio (O/I). When employees believe that their O/I ratio is equal to the referent's O/I ratio, they reach the conclusion that they are being treated fairly. However, when employees believe that their O/I ratio is different from their referent's O/I, then they conclude that they are being treated unfairly.

The two types of inequity are under reward and over reward. Under reward takes place when an employee's O/I ratio is worse than his referent's O/I. Over reward takes place when the employee's O/I is better than his referent's O/I. An employee is getting more outcomes in relation to his inputs than his referent is. Some employees would feel guilt from this.

When motivating the different generations in the workplace utilizing the equity theory, managers and supervisors need to seek out and ensure that all inequities are corrected. Employers can reduce employee's inputs. Employers can discover and eliminate the percent of their job that does not increase productivity. The companies' human resources managers, middle managers, and first line supervisors should ensure that the decision-making processes are fair.

Expectancy Theory

According to Mulcahy (2002), the expectancy theory is that employees will be motivated when they believe that their efforts will lead to good performance, and that their good performance will be rewarded and the rewards will be attractive. Expectancy theory components are valence, expectancy, and instrumentality. Valence is desirability and attractiveness. Expectancy is the perceived relationship between effort and performance.

When employees' expectancies are strong, then the employees believe that their diligent work and efforts will result in good performance which makes the employees work harder. The opposite happens when employees have low expectancies. Instrumentality is the understanding relationship between performance and rewards. When the instrumentality is strong, employees believe that improved performance will lead to more rewards.

Lawler, Porter, and Vroom (2009) stated that the expectancy theory equation can be represented by the following: Valence x Expectancy x Instrumentality = Motivation.

If there is a decline in any one of the variables, then there will be a decline in the employees' motivation. When motivating the different generations in the workplace utilizing the expectancy theory, managers and supervisors need to collect information to find out what the employees want from their jobs. This can be accomplished by managers and supervisors asking the employees directly what it is they want from their employment.

Managers and supervisors can take certain steps to connect rewards to individual performances. This must be articulated in a clear and precise way to the employees. The companies' managers and supervisors should empower the employees to make decisions if they want the employees to believe that their hard work and efforts will lead to good performance. When utilized correctly and appropriately, rewards can motivate employees and bring cohesiveness among employees from the different generations.

Reinforcement Theory

Reinforcement theory states that behavior is a function of its consequences which means that behaviors followed by positive consequences will occur more frequently than those followed by negative consequences. There are two parts to reinforcement theory. The reinforcement contingencies are the cause and effect relationships between the performance of specific behavior and consequences. The schedule of reinforcement is rules pertaining to reinforcement contingencies such as which behavior will be reinforced, which consequences will follow behaviors, and the schedule by which those consequences will be delivered (Dickinson and Poling, 1996).

The components of the reinforcement theory are positive reinforcement, negative reinforcement, punishment reinforcement, and extinction reinforcement. The managers and supervisors utilize these reinforcement methods for controlling the behavior of the workers. Positive reinforcement strengthens behavior by following behaviors with desirable consequences. Negative reinforcement strengthens behavior by withholding an undesirable consequence when employees perform a certain behavior. Also, the employees perform a behavior to prevent a negative consequence.

Punishment weakens behavior by following behaviors with unpleasant consequences. For example, companies have a disciplinary policy where the employees are given an oral warning first, then if the incident occurs again, the employees will receive a written warning, then time off without pay. The employer wants you to think about your inappropriate actions at work. If the inappropriate action happens again, then the employee will be terminated. Extinction is a reinforcement tactic in which a positive consequence is no longer followed by a reinforced behavior. Extinction weakens the behaviors, lowering the probability that it will happen.

There are two categories of reinforcement schedules which are continuous and intermittent. With continuous reinforcement schedules, a consequence follows every instance of a behavior. For example, the more an employee produces the more that employee earns. The intermittent reinforcement schedules consequences are delivered after a specified or average time has passed. Two of these reinforcement schedules are based on time. The fixed interval reinforcement schedules consequences follow a behavior after a fixed time has passed. The variable interval reinforcement schedules consequences follow a behavior after different times.

When motivating the different generations in the workplace utilizing reinforcement theory, the managers and supervisors must identify the important observable performance related behaviors, analyze the causes and consequences of these behaviors in the workplace, intervene by utilizing positive and negative reinforcement to increase the frequency of these important behaviors, and evaluate the extent to which intervention actually changes the employees' behavior. The managers and supervisors should not reinforce the wrong behaviors. The managers and supervisors should dispense the appropriate punishment at the appropriate time. Finally, the managers and supervisors should choose the simplest and most effective schedule of reinforcement pertaining to that individual.

Goal Setting Theory

Goal setting theory states that employees will be motivated when they accept certain challenging objectives and receive feedback that will indicate their progress toward achieving those objectives. The components of goal setting theory are goal specificity, goal difficulty, goal acceptance, and performance feedback (Latham and Locke, 2006). Goal specificity is specific, detailed goals for the individual. Goal difficulty is the scope and range in which a goal is challenging to achieve. Goal acceptance is the extent to which people understand and agree to the goal (Latham and Locke, 2006). This is the same as goal commitment. The individual must find the goal a benefit, and that it is achievable (Latham and Locke, 2006)

If the goal is not measureable, specific, and realistic, then this would lower the motivation and commitment of the individual (Bennett, 2009). When the individual achieves the goal, this success will raise their boundary goals to new levels, resulting in improvement in work performance (Corker and Donnellan, 2012). The last step would be feedback on the individual progress on achieving the goal. Feedback is necessary in keeping the goals effective and flexible (Bennett, 2009). Employees will increase their efforts and performance to achieve a goal if the rewards are available and attractive (Presslee, Vance, and Webb, 2013).

Asplund and Blacksmith (2013) found that employees who set goals that were based on their personal strengths were seven times more likely to be engaged in their work assigned and be high performers. It is imperative that in setting goals for anybody, the S.M.A.R.T. guidelines be utilized. S.M.A.R.T. goals are specific, measurable, attainable, realistic, and timely (Loehr and Kaye, 2011). This should appeal to the different generations in setting goals.

This brings us to management by objectives. Management by objectives is a four-step process in goal setting. The manager and the individual talk about and select a goal. The manager and the individual develop tactical plans and meet regularly for feedback on progress. People must set goals and pursue them (Halvorson, 2010). The managers and supervisors should always follow a goal setting process (Adams, 2013).

Transformational Leadership for Motivating and Cohesiveness the Four Generations

Transformational leadership can motivate, inspire, and bring cohesiveness to people of all generations. Transformational leadership can generate motivation, cohesiveness, productivity, performance, and morale through mechanisms, characteristics, and style. Transformational leaders can articulate a vision for the future.

In transformational leadership, it is the leader who must have the self-assurance, charisma, confidence, and belief that he or she can personally make a difference and impact on employees, organizations, groups, and people (Benson, 2008). This includes people of different generations. Transformational leadership goes further than participatory leadership, situational leadership, and transactional leadership by being aware and accepting the organization's purpose and mission, and by getting the employees, organizations, groups, and people to see beyond their own needs and self-interest for the betterment of all.

During crisis and ethical dilemma, transformational leaders try to obtain from the employees, organizations, groups, and people every ounce of their energies and drives to accomplish more than they thought was possible to bring about change and create a culture of motivation, cohesiveness, and ethical behavior. According to Conger (1999), the fundamental elements of transformation influence that leaders use to induce or bring about change are influencing followers by establishing a vision for a better future, inspiring followers as opposed to controlling them, leading by example through role modeling, contributing to subordinates' intellectual stimulation, enhancing meaningfulness of goals and behaviors, fulfilling followers' self-actualization needs, empowering followers through intrinsic motivation, exhibiting confidence in subordinates' ability to attain higher levels of achievement, and enhancing collective identity.

Transformational leaders should influence followers by articulating a new and clear vision. The transformational leaders get their followers to undertake long journeys to improve the future of the organization, not because they are easy but because they are difficult. A transformational leader can establish a culture of motivation, cohesiveness, and ethical behavior in the organization. Transformational leaders can inspire employees, organizations, groups, and people instead of deceiving and controlling them.

Leaders should respect and have a desire to serve. General Colin Powell could be a transformational leader. The former Chairman of the Joint Chiefs of Staff and Secretary of State projects authority, confidence, charisma, and substance to people of all ages. General Powell (2012) discussed in his book *It Worked for Me: In life and Leadership*, lessons learned through his time in leadership in the military and in civilian life. General Powell is proud of his appeal to all ages. He could provide transformational leadership that will motivate, inspire, and bring cohesiveness to all people of different generations. General Powell can clearly articulate the vision for the future of a company.

According to White and Prywes (2007), General Powell fits into the *Great Leaders* category because he is a visionary, inspiring, versatile, risk taker, giant, builder, and a legend.

President John F. Kennedy was a transformational leader. He articulated a vision for the country in civil rights and space travel. In President Kennedy's inaugural address when he said that "the torch has been passed to a new generation," it gave people goose bumps. The nation was inspired and motivated.

President Kennedy had confidence and charisma. People who met him in person came away liking him. If you want to be a transformational leader, then the ability to inspire people is not optional but it is critical (Barnes, 2005). Transformational leaders believe in leading by example. This way, one can change employees, organizations, groups, and people's attitudes and values to get the desired results of behaviors. Transformational leaders have the ability to be influential and charismatic.

Transformational leaders can contribute to employees, organizations, groups, and people's intellectual encouragement and emotional intelligence. The leaders must provide higher frequency information and seek feedback from subordinates.

Transformational leaders must have strong values and inspire subordinates to follow in order to achieve the organizational objectives.

Transformational leaders need to fulfill subordinates' self-actualization needs. Again, we see Maslow's Hierarchy of Needs being utilized to get subordinates to work toward the organizational objectives. Maslow's self-actualization needs consist of morality, creativity, spontaneity, problem-solving, lack of prejudice, and acceptance of facts. The employees, organizations, groups, and people need to be recognized for their contributions and treated as valuable assets.

Transformational leaders must empower employees, organizations, groups, and people through intrinsic motivation. The leaders must ensure that they make every effort to get all their employees emotionally committed for the betterment of the company. Leaders must encourage employees, organizations, groups, and people to identify and solve problems themselves. For transformational leaders, providing empowerment is their way of showing that they trust the employees, organizations, groups, and people. With this trusting relationship, the employees, organizations, groups, and people would work to accomplish the objectives. Transformational leaders have the ability to create and maintain a collective identity with the employees, organizations, groups, and people.

President John F. Kennedy and General Colin Powell embodied Kouzes and Posner's five practices of the Exemplary Leadership Model. The five practices of the Exemplary Leadership Model are: model the way, inspire a shared vision, challenge the process, enable others to act, and encourage the heart. Modeling the way is when leaders realize and explain values by finding their way, producing shared ideas, and providing the examples by aligning actions with shared values.

When leaders model the way, they treat subordinates with honesty, fairness, dignity, and respect. General Powell led by example to show the subordinates that he would not ask them to do activities that he was not willing to accept or do. He would provide subordinates the vision, mission, and goals, and establish a road map for pursuing the goals, as well as assisting in developing personal goals of the subordinates. He would provide a set of short-term, less difficult goals that the subordinates could achieve to build their confidence to work toward more challenging and aggressive goals for the long-term. He would share his ideas and goals with the subordinates so there would be no misunderstanding in pursuing the organizational and personal goals.

Using the model enables others to act. Leaders must seek and build trust and facilitate relationship through collaboration. Through the collaboration process, the subordinates feel like they are contributing and doing their part in making tasks, activities, and situations a success, giving them a sense of worth and accomplishment. General Powell believed in utilizing the collaboration approach to gain all the subordinate inputs and feedbacks. This is one of the ways to build an atmosphere of trust, goodwill, and dignity. The encourage heart model is when leaders recognize an individual's important contributions to the organization by expressing appreciation for assignments well done. The leader would single out subordinates or teams for jobs well done.

Path-Goal Theory/Leadership Theory

Path-goal theory involves increasing the employee's motivation and satisfaction by developing paths to high performance and high rewards for achieving objectives (House and Mitchell, 1974). Managers and supervisors produce what is called a road map of each individual linear and non-linear success in the organization. Managers and supervisors will delineate how subordinates can achieve team and organization goals, and take care of issues and barriers that prevent them from succeeding (House and Mitchell, 1974).

Managers and supervisors should increase the number and types of rewards for achievement of the objectives. The managers and supervisors should do things today to influence employees that will lead to future rewards and satisfaction. Also, the managers and supervisors should offer employees from different generations something different and valuable. People must set goals and pursue them (Halvorson, 2010).

Culture: National Culture/Organizational Culture

In today's workplace, culture and national culture are linked together. Companies employ people from all over the globe. Today, managers and supervisors need to be aware of this important aspect of culture in managing today's workforce. Culture is a defined system of behaviors, values, beliefs, norms, shared motives, and traditions which are transmitted through generations (House, 1971). Culture is a learned pattern of behavior in people's lives. These are components of society that create feelings of belonging and togetherness among people.

According to House (1971), culture will influence leadership and organizational practices. Managers and supervisors can benefit from information on the behaviors and organizational practices that are acceptable and unacceptable (House, 1971). Culture encompasses various aspects of communication, attitude, and etiquette. Every society has a different culture which gives it an identity and uniqueness. In the vast cultural diversity, there are certain elements of culture that are universal. Hofstede (2001) says, cultural differences will influence behavior, perception, and understanding.

Culture is the cohesiveness that joins people together. Culture is connected to the development of one's attitude. It gives an individual his or her unique identity. Culture can be shared and learned as well. Some additional elements of culture are language, religion, social collectives, cultural integration, role in society, and status. It is up to the leader of the company to play the critical role in successfully establishing the principles of culture that an organization will be following to achieve the goals of the company (Schein, 2010).

There are key resources for understanding and changing organizational culture to make an organization more effective such as systematic strategy and methodology (Cameron and Quinn, 2011). The key factors to successful organizational culture are adaptability, flexibility, employee involvement, core beliefs that are widely shared throughout and held, and company vision. The company vision can be a powerful strategy for the organizational culture to build around.

The merger of culture and organizational change can improve performance (Schein, 2009). According to *Managing Change in Organization: A practice guide* (Project Management Institute, 2013), culture can provide motivation and cohesion throughout the company. The culture is critical to a company's survival. There are four environmental factors affecting cultural: high level of education, social networking, cultural shift, and social pressures. Since culture affects motivation and cohesion throughout a company, culture needs to be considered when thinking about implementing significant changes in a company.

STRATEGIES FOR RECRUITMENT AND RETENTION OF THE FOUR DIFFERENT GENERATIONS IN THE WORKPLACE RECRUITMENT/HIRING

Traditionalists

For Traditionalists, companies should offer utilization of a combination of current technology and traditional methods, such as classified ads in the newspaper, employment publications, online job search engines, and networking (Zemke et al., 2013). Companies can provide address, telephone, and fax numbers for resumes. Climbing the corporate ladder is probably not a motivating force now (Marston, 2007). It is important to tell Traditionalists that their skill sets and experiences are critically needed, and that younger employees can learn from them. They will be given the assignments, and can use their own initiatives to get the mission accomplished. They have the freedom and empowerment to operate in the organization. Of course, status reports will have to be provided (Brokaw, 1998). Companies must be able to offer Traditionalists a wide spectrum of opportunities to join their company. Companies must offer flexible working options, such as working part-time, working from home, and commuting from home to office expenses.

The Baby Boomers

The companies must offer competitive salaries, prestigious titles, and recognition to the Baby Boomers (Steinhorn, 2006). Companies must offer Baby Boomers a fancy office with plenty of space. Companies must offer empowerment and annual performance review to ensure that they are heading in the planned direction. Companies must support political freedom. The companies must allow Baby Boomers to build a career.

Gen Xers

What companies can offer to the Gen Xers is the utilization of high technological equipment. Companies can offer online employment applications and methods to the Gen Xers. Potential employers can provide the latest websites, company smartphones, social media sites, and keep their website information up-to-date (Gordinier, 2008). Companies should provide a well described job description. Companies must offer a balanced work life for Gen Xers (Shaw, 2013). The companies must offer family like events, for example, monthly barbecue events for employees' families (Zemke et al., 2013).

Millennials

To appeal to Millennials, companies must offer good salaries and signing incentives, as these are the expectations of this generation. Companies must provide the latest technological tools to them to do their work. Companies must offer smartphones, social media access, and powerful communicating devices. Companies must also have social events for employees. The companies should offer Millennials flexible work environments and multiple forms of technologies for their applications (Erickson, 2008).

Companies should offer mentorship programs to this generation, and be sure to inform this generation that the company utilizes state-of-the-art technology. Companies must offer social events for their employees to get to know other employees in the company, for example, the company can sponsor some sports events for their employees. These companies will allow this generation to build parallel careers (Gordinier, 2008).

RETENTION

Traditionalists

The company must offer competitive salaries. However, for Traditionalists, salary may not be only thing that drives or motivates them. Traditionalists will not be motivated by fancy titles. Companies must remember that Traditionalists are working because of social outlets and to have an income to supplement their golden years. They enjoy being around and conversing with people (Shaw, 2013). Companies should allow choices in benefits for the Traditionalists, such as long-term disability, long-term health insurance, and problem counselors on a twenty-four-hour phone line.

In difficult economic times, the companies should have a plan to reduce work hours, or furlough workers instead of terminating. Traditionalists would consider this as the company taking care of them. Traditionalists believe that if they are loyal to the company, then the company will take care of them.

Companies should provide challenging assignments where employees' knowledge and years of experiences can be utilized to the fullest. Traditionalists can be placed with working teams or brainstorming groups. Traditionalists can mentor the younger generations (Lancaster and Stillman, 2005). Companies must offer flexible working options, such as working part-time, working from home, and expense accounts for commuting from home to the office.

Baby Boomers

For the Baby Boomers, companies must offer competitive salaries and opportunities for promotions and personal growth (Steinhorn, 2006). Companies should allow choices for this generation, such as referral services for childcare and paid time off to take care of sick children and parents. Companies should provide Baby Boomers challenging assignments that will allow them to advance their careers through promotions. Companies should also provide this generation with opportunities for job rotation to prevent the burnout syndrome. The majority of Baby Boomers might be thinking of retiring in five to ten years, so companies should be seeking other ways and methods to keep them at their desks.

Gen Xers

Companies must provide opportunities for Gen Xers to work independently and not be micromanaged. Companies must offer competitive salaries, benefit packages, and advancement for leadership positions in the future. This generation wants a balance with companies (Gordinier, 2008). Companies should provide choices for time off for sick children's care, paid time off for parents to take their children to daycare centers, and flexibility in work hours in the office.

Companies should provide the Gen Xers with challenging assignments that will increase their skill sets, knowledge, and experience.

Millennials

The companies should ensure that there are processes and procedures in place where frequent feedback on their performance is provided in a timely fashion. The companies should offer Millennials flexible work environments and multiple forms of technologies for their applications (Erickson, 2008). Companies should provide flexibility in salaries and health insurance options for the Millennials.

To keep Millennials happy, companies should provide assignments that are important and have a definite purpose. The manager and supervisor should provide frequent feedback on their performance. Managers and supervisors should explain to Millennials how they can contribute to the success of the company and provide opportunities to go back to school to work on advance degrees that will improve their performance in the company (Shaw, 2013). The companies must continue to provide learning opportunities, and realize that this generation will be going through learning curves in order to acquire knowledge, conflict resolution skills, negotiating skills, and experience.

Millennials will already possess technological equipment and online method skills in terms of computer skills, software skills, and social media skills (Zemke et al., 2013). By understanding the characteristics of the different generations in the workplace, Millennials will be respected and valued for their contributions to the company. This is what Millennials want from other generations in the workplace. For Millennials, slowly climbing the corporate ladder is no longer a motivational force (Marston, 2007).

SUMMARY

There are many books and articles dealing with this phenomenon of the four different generations in the workplace from a motivational aspect. Drucke (2002), pointed out:

> "Older generation rapid growth in population in the workplaces and the rapid shrinking of the younger generation and that a growing number of older people over fifty will not keep on working as traditional full time-time nine to five employees, but will participate in the labor force as part-timers, consultants and temporaries." (pp. 235–236)

Motivational issues, cohesive issues and tensions between the different generations can escalate when managers and supervisors impetuously attempt to apply the same motivational and cohesiveness methods to everybody. There is no *one size* strategy that fits the four different generations in the workplace. When managers and supervisors reluctantly attempt to motivate the employees with one method for all, it will not lead to increased performance and cohesiveness in achieving the goals of the organization. This could lead to confusion in the organization.

Companies look to increase their bottom lines by using transparent, positive stories to enhance their image toward technologically-advanced customers by utilizing all of the talent, creativity, and innovative concepts from the four different generations working together in a motivated and cohesive fashion to support and achieve the goals of the organization. Managers and supervisors must change their priorities when the situations dictate when they are dealing with the four different generations. By utilizing the proper effective motivational theories and methods such as McGregor's Theory, Maslow's Hierarchy of Needs, Alderfer's ERG Theory, McClelland's Learned Needs Theory, Herzberg's Two-Factor Theory of Motivation, Intrinsic Motivation, Extrinsic Motivation, Equity Theory,

Expectancy Theory, Reinforcement Theory, Goal Setting Theory, Transformational Leadership, Path-Goal Theory, Organizational Culture, and Strategies for Recruitment and Retention motivation, cohesiveness and performance can be increased among the four different generations in the workplaces.

CHAPTER 3

METHODOLOGY

I n utilizing the qualitative method approach, this research study explored the motivating theories and methods that will increase motivation and cohesiveness between the four different generations in the workplace. This is the first time in the history of the workplace where you have four different and unique generations coming together in the workplace. The four different generations working in the same environment in today's contemporary workplace is a phenomenon.

The research study was based on some of the motivating theories and methods that will increase the motivation and cohesiveness among the four different generations in the workplace to support and achieve the goals of the organization. Managers and supervisors must understand the generational differences in regard to performance, recruiting, retaining, and managing employees in the workplace because each generation has its own beliefs, norms, cultures, religions, and social structure (Shaw, 2013). The methods and organizations used to motivate and bring about cohesiveness among the four different generations will be extremely significant in achieving the goals of the organization.

All the generations view situations from their own generational perspectives, and each generation is motivated differently (Lancaster and Stillman, 2005). It is very important that companies realize this so that a more customized plan and strategy can be assembled together for the different generations. How these different generations are motivated will determine the bottom line of the company. In today's workplace, we have the Traditionalists, Baby Boomers, Gen Xers, and Millennial generations.

RESEARCH DESIGN

Based on the phenomena that have been identified, it would be best to research utilizing the qualitative methodologies in conjunction with the phenomenological approach for this research design study. The qualitative research phenomenology method explores some of the motivational theories and methods used to increase motivation and cohesiveness among the four different generations in the workplace. Qualitative research is a way to understand and examine the individual or group issues that attribute to social or human problems.

The reason for the phenomenological method approach is for the researchers to identify the phenomena through their actual life experience. Phenomenology is concerned with the study of experience from the perspective of the researchers with the participants. Phenomenological studies are based in patterns and examples of the researchers having personal knowledge and subjectivity. However, in the phenomenological approach, the researchers bracket or segregate his or her experiences to understand those who participate in the study (Nieswiadomy and Cobb, 1993).

Phenomenological studies make detailed notes about the participant's situation and do not project themselves to direct generalization. Pure phenomenological research seeks to describe rather than explain, and to start from a perspective free from hypotheses or preconceptions (Husserl, 1970). The phenomenological purpose is to gather detailed descriptions and understand a specific phenomenon.

In research design, phenomenological is non-experimental, qualitative, and descriptive. Phenomenology is a theory related to understanding the human experience and attempting to control bias. Phenomenological studies describe and interpret the experience of the research participants to understand the human experience of the individual and oneself.

One of the conditions of phenomenological studies is that the researchers must have the same experience as the participant. This equates to the old saying "walking in the same path" of the specific participant. Phenomenological studies focus on understanding, meaning, and interaction with the participants, usually through a single central question in the research.

In a phenomenology study, the researcher seeks the essence or root causes of the phenomenon. Phenomenology is considered a philosophical and qualitative research approach (Kerry and Armour, 2000; Madjar and Walton, 1999). Phenomenology attempts to provide explanations and meaning for human experience. Phenomenologists want to understand how the world appears to others.

In phenomenology, transcript analyses of written transcripts and audio tapes are performed after the entire transcription from the participant's interview has been completed (LoBiondo-Wood, Haber, and Krainovich-Miller, 1999). Phenomenology offers reports of "experienced space, time, body, and human relationship as we live them" (Van Maanen, 2000). There have been steps identified in phenomenological data analysis, such as obtaining the sense of the phenomenon in its entirety and segregating interview data into smaller compartments pertaining to the phenomenon. In phenomenology, the participants are chosen because they have lived the experiences that are being studied, and they are willing to share their thoughts on the research subject.

In phenomenology, the data collection method is an in-depth interview with semi-structured or unstructured, open-ended questions that are utilized to extract more accurate and precise information. The relative information is extracted from the final transcription and then evaluated. For phenomenological studies, the data analysis starts with the researcher's experiences with the phenomenon. The researchers identify data in the interviews that show the phenomenon. Components are formed from the statements, and an overall account of the meaning of the experience is formulated.

Phenomenological researchers utilize a method called bracketing to ensure that the researcher is not affected by his own bias.

Population

The population of this study came from utilizing the convenience sample method which include colleagues, business associates, and acquaintances. The qualitative research collected and gathered information from the chosen participants by interviews and observations during the interview period.

Sample

The specification of the purposeful sample were participants from the researcher's colleagues and acquaintances. The participant's ages ranged from twenty-two-year-olds to sixty-nine-year-olds. The participants were male and female, with different backgrounds and years of education. The researcher utilized the convenience sample method, and arranged the place and time of the researcher choosing for the interview.

The names of the participants in the study and sample will be kept confidential. The participants consisted of 50% males.

Participants

Participants from each of the four generations were selected. For the focus group, there was one person from each generation selected. Some of the participants were from engineering, marketing, sales, services, and finances.

Research Question

The research question is: What are the different methods, theories, or activities of motivation that can be utilized by managers and supervisors to make the four different generations work together effectively and efficiently in the workplace, and enhance motivational efforts among each of these generational groups?

Interview Questions

1. Would you provide information based on your actual working experience with the different generations pertaining to what seems to motivate and drive them to success in the company?

2. When you are working with someone from a different generation, which generation do you think each individual fits into, and what do you think could be done to make your experience more effective or efficient?

3. When you are working with someone from another generation, did you notice a difference in demeanor pertaining to behavior, different style of thinking, and performance that is associated with those specific generations?

4. What motivates you to do the best you can in achieving the goals of the organization, and what do you think it would take to motivate the other generations (e.g., gifts, salary, promotions, rewards, recognition, pride, sense of achievement, or a feeling of a job well done)?

5. What do you enjoy the most about working with each of the four generations, and what did you like the least about it?

6. When working with someone from a different generation, which generations do you think preferred the extrinsic or intrinsic rewards to make them work more effectively and efficiently?

7. What are some of the things you could learn from the other generations that will make you better at your jobs?

8. In working with members from other generations, what generations do you believe fit into the following, and please elaborate:
   - Need to be told what to do at work
   - Need to be watched and micromanaged for their assignments at work
   - Want to work unsupervised and have the freedom to make decisions at work
   - Have an aspiration to maintain interpersonal relations with people
   - Have requirements of affiliation, achievement, and power
   - Have desires for self-development and personal growth

9. Speaking for your own generation, which of these factors are important: pay, fringe benefits, physical working conditions, status, interpersonal relations, and job security? Please elaborate on your response.

10. Speaking for your own generation, what are your feelings toward job recognition, sense of achievement, growth, and promotional opportunities in the workplace? Please elaborate on your response.

11. Would you explain or please feel free to elaborate your expectations and perceptions in working with the other generations? Are you fairly treated in relation to others by the company, or is it the perception that you are being unfairly treated?

12. Do you believe that your efforts will lead to a good performance and that good performance will be rewarded and the rewards will be attractive? Please elaborate on your response.

13. In working with other members of a different generation, would you believe that their behavior is a function of its consequences, which means that behaviors followed by positive consequences will occur more frequently than those followed by negative consequences?

14. In working with members from the other generations, would you elaborate on transformational leadership from the perspective that motivation and inspiration can bring cohesiveness to people of all generations? For example, somebody like Dr. Martin Luther King, President Kennedy, President Obama, or General Colin Powell could provide this transformational leadership?

15. When working with the members from the other generations, how important is organizational culture?

16. Would you elaborate on the importance of your manager and you developing paths to high performance and high rewards for achieving the objective or a goal setting process that will assist you in your career?

17. What are your company's strategies for recruiting and retaining talented people from the four different generations for the company?

Interviews/Interview Protocol

The researcher ensured that each member of the four different generations was represented at the interview. The researcher followed an interview protocol when asking questions and recording responses during a qualitative interview (Creswell 2009). The participants were provided with the dates and times of the interview.

The researcher made the participants feel relaxed and put their minds at ease. The researcher explained to the participants the objective, data collection methods, and analysis method of the research. The researcher explained the benefit or benefits of the research.

Managing the different generations increases cohesiveness and motivation to support and achieve the organizational goals. The researcher provided the guidelines for the interview. The participants could take as much time as they wanted to complete the interview questions.

The researcher did not want the participants to be under any mental or physical pressures. The interview was one-on-one. The researcher explained that there was no right or wrong answer. The researcher explained the benefits of the research. This was simply a chance to learn and talk about the four different generations working together in today's workplace.

The participant's identities and confidentiality will be legally protected. The responses to the interview questions will be locked in a safe, and can only be accessed by the researcher. The researcher provided a thank you statement at the end of the interview to acknowledge the time and date of the interview (Creswell 2009).

Procedures

The participants were provided with the instructions and materials that will be utilized during the interview. The data gathering instrument was a set of interview questions. The time allotted for going over of each participant's responses to the interview questions was one hour. The researcher took notes of the conversations and met with the participants to review and to ensure that the notes are accurate in their meaning and intentions (Creswell, 2009).

Validity

The interview was structured. In conducting structured, open-ended interview, the researcher was able to obtain the views, opinions, and more detailed information from the participants. The researcher conducted the interview face-to-face. Phenomenological research utilizes the analysis of critical statements, generating units, and the formation of what Moustakas (1994) referred to as essence description about the phenomenon described by the participants (Creswell, 2009). There are procedures for validating the data.

Validation of Data

The note transcriptions were provided back to the participants to review for accuracy and approval prior to the data analysis and interpretation phase of the research study. This researcher acknowledges his bias in the study being from the Baby Boomers' generation.

Data Collection/Data Analysis

Data collection methods were subjective and narrative for results, small numbers, non-statistical analysis, and non-numerical. The results of the interviews were utilized to assess the managing of the different generations to increase cohesiveness and motivation through different methods, theories, or activities of motivation that enhance motivational efforts among each generation.

Ethics and Confidentiality

The identities and confidentiality of the participants will be legally protected. The professional conduct practitioners, researchers, students, and seasoned veterans are governed by the ethical principles and guidelines in the Publication Manual of the American Psychological Association (APA, 2010). The researcher followed the requirements of the IRB because the rights and welfare of the participants are of paramount concern (Cone and Foster, 1993).

SUMMARY

This chapter covered the methodology which was the qualitative method with the phenomenological approach to study and explore the motivating theories and methods that will increase motivation and cohesiveness between the four generations in the workplace.

The population, sample, participants, research question, interview, validity, procedures, data collection/analysis, ethics, and confidentiality are all explained in the chapter. The participants came from colleagues, business associates, and acquaintances.

FINDINGS

RESTATEMENT OF THE PURPOSE

The purpose of the study was to investigate how to manage the four different generations in order to increase cohesiveness and motivation in the workplace and to ascertain which methods, theories, or activities of motivation can be utilized to enhance motivation and cohesiveness among each generation and minimize collisions and clashes among the generations when their behavior collide and clash among the generations and their behavior, beliefs, cultures, norms, agenda, values, priorities and work ethic differ. Data was collected from interviews and focus group and the utilization of this information is included in this research study.

Research Study Preparation

The research participants were chosen utilizing the convenience sample method. The purposeful sample included participants from each generation and the ages ranged from twenty–two to sixty–nine years old with different backgrounds, educational levels, and disciplines. Also, the focus group utilized participants from each generation to gather data in multiple ways and from different sources. This is known as the triangulation of data method. For the focus group, there were four different generations research participants used in the study.

The interview approach was to make the participants as relaxed as possible. The objective, data collection, and analysis methods of research were explained to the participants. The potential benefit or benefits of the research were explained to the participants.

The interviewer's questions were designed to help understand and seek out the different generations' motivation and cohesiveness factors that will enable them to work together in the workplace more effectively and efficiently to achieve the goals of the organization. The guidelines for the interview were provided to the participants (e.g., if the participant wants a drink of water or to go to the restroom, then the interview will stop). It was explained to the research participants that there are no right or wrong answers during the interview. This is simply a chance to learn and talk about the four different generations working together effectively and efficiently in today's workplace. The researcher did not want the participants to be under any mental or physical pressure for the interview.

INTERVIEW QUESTIONS/MANAGING THE DIFFERENT GENERATIONS IN ORDER TO INCREASE COHESIVENESS AND MOTIVATION IN THE WORKPLACE

1. Would you provide information based on your actual working experience with the different generations pertaining to what seems to motivate and drive them to success in the company?
2. When you are working with someone from a different generation, which generation do you think each individual fits into, and what do you think could be done to make your experience more effective or efficient?
3. When you are working with someone from another generation, did you notice a difference in demeanor pertaining to behavior, different style of thinking, and performance that is associated with those specific generations?

4. What motivates you to do the best you can in achieving the goals of the organization, and what do you think it would take to motivate the other generations (e.g., gifts, salary, promotions, rewards, recognition, pride, sense of achievement, or a feeling of a job well done)?

5. What do you enjoy the most about working with each of the four generations, and what did you like the least about it?

6. When working with someone from a different generation, which generations do you think preferred the extrinsic or intrinsic rewards to make them work more effectively and efficiently?

7. What are some of the things you could learn from the other generations that will make you better at your job?

8. In working with members from other generations, what generations do you believe fit into the following and please elaborate:
   - Need to be told what to do at work
   - Need to be watched and micromanaged for their assignments at work
   - Want to work unsupervised and have the freedom to make decisions at work
   - Have an aspiration to maintain interpersonal relations with people
   - Have requirements of affiliation, achievement, and power
   - Have desires for self-development and personal growth

9. Speaking for your own generation, which of these factors are important: pay, fringe benefits, physical working conditions, status, interpersonal relations, and job security? Please elaborate on your response.

10. Speaking for your own generation, what are your feelings toward job recognition, sense of achievement, growth, and promotional opportunities in the workplace? Please elaborate on your response.

11. Would you explain or please feel free to elaborate your expectations and perceptions in working with the other

generations? Are you fairly treated in relation to others by the company, or is it the perception that you are being unfairly treated?

12. Do you believe that your efforts will lead to a good performance and that good performance will be rewarded and the rewards will be attractive? Please elaborate on your response.

13. In working with other members of a different generation, would you believe that their behavior is a function of its consequences, which means that behaviors followed by positive consequences will occur more frequently than those followed by negative consequences?

14. In working with members from the other generations, would you elaborate on transformational leadership from the perspective that motivation and inspiration can bring cohesiveness to people of all generations? For example, somebody like President Kennedy, Dr. Martin Luther King, President Reagan, President Obama, or General Colin Powell could provide this transformational leadership?

15. When working with the members from the other generations, how important is organizational culture?

16. Would you elaborate on the importance of your manager and you developing paths to high performance and high rewards for achieving the objective or a goal setting process that will assist you in your career?

17. What are your company's strategies for recruiting and retaining talented people from the four different generations for the company?

QUALITATIVE DATA COLLECTION

The qualitative data collection types that were utilized in this research were face-to-face and one-on-one interviews, and by observations of the participants during the interview process. The observation of the nonverbal communications of the participants during the interview and with the focus group interview and discussion were collected.

The written documents, transcripts, and notes of the responses from the research participants were collected. The interviewer's questions were open-ended questions that were designed to obtain detailed description information about the different generations.

Validity

The research participants received the written documents that contained their responses for them to review for accuracy and for their signatures if they agreed that what was written down was correct. The focus group provided triangulation data from multiple sources and was utilized as validity strategies (Creswell, 2009). Detailed description information was obtained from the participants during the interviews. The triangulation data provided collaborating data for the research in terms of findings.

Data Analysis

Themes and broad patterns begin to emerge by analyzing and evaluating the responses from the participants. The research participants' responses were read over again and dissected to arrive at the interpretations (Lincoln and Guba, 1985).

Findings

After analyzing, evaluating, and interpreting the responses provided by the research participants, the following themes and patterns emerged:

> Theme 1: Motivation and cohesiveness factors for each generation
> Theme 2: Different characteristics of the four different generations

Theme 3: Stress among the different generations in workplace

Theme 4: Importance of developing and setting goals/ objectives

Theme 5: Identifying the behavior, different style of thinking, and performance

Theme 6: Generations getting along with each other in the workplace

Theme 7: Managing the different generations to work effectively and efficiently utilizing extrinsic and intrinsic rewards

Theme 8: Good performances will lead to attractive rewards

Theme 9: Transformational leadership can provide motivation, inspiration, and cohesiveness among the different generations

Theme 10: Organizational Culture can provide motivation, cohesion, and improve performance

Theme 11: Theories for managing and motivating the four different generations

Theme 12: Behavior is a function of its consequences

Theme 13: Strategies for recruiting and retaining talented people from the four different generations

THEME 1: MOTIVATION AND COHESIVENESS FACTOR FOR EACH GENERATION

Question 1: *Would you provide information or observation based on your actual working experience with the different generations pertaining to what seems to motivate and drive them to success in the company?*
Question 4: *What motivates you to do the best you can in achieving the goals of the organization, and what do you think it would take to motivate the other generations (e.g., gifts, salary, promotions, rewards, recognition, pride, sense of achievement, or a feeling of a job well done)?*
Question 6: *When working with someone from a different genera-*

tion, which generations do you think preferred the extrinsic or intrinsic rewards to make them work more effectively and efficiently? Question 9: *Speaking for your own generation, which of these factors is important: pay, fringe benefits, physical working conditions, status, interpersonal relations, and job security? Please elaborate on your response.* Question 10: *Speaking for your own generation, what are your feelings toward job recognition, sense of achievement, growth, and promotional opportunities in the workplace? Please elaborate on your response.* The responses revealed by the research participants that each generation had different motivations and cohesiveness factors that contributed to their performances and togetherness in terms of economic incentives, recognition, praise, and achieving objectives. These extrinsic and intrinsic rewards seem to generate the theme. This theme was consistent with most of the responses.

Here are a few of the pertinent quotes:

Traditionalists—A combination of all the things mentioned in question 4 (DG004). Baby Boomers—Are motivated by salary, formal meetings, and competition (DG006). Gen Xers—Xers want to be compensated sufficiently for their performances (DG010). Millennials—The latest technological tools for them to do their work. Good salaries and flexible work environment (DG012).

THEME 2: DIFFERENT CHARACTERISTICS OF THE FOUR DIFFERENT GENERATIONS

Question 1: *Would you provide information or observation based on your actual working experience with the different generations pertaining to what seems to motivate and drive them to success in the company?* The responses showed that participants were aware of the different characteristics of the four generations. This theme was consistent with most of the responses.

Here are a few of the pertinent quotes:

Traditionalists—Glad to have a job and work hard. Would retire with the same company. Baby Boomers—Many went to college to get a degree and a good job. Work hard to get ahead. Likely to retire with the same company. Gen Xers/Generation X—Many getting a degree. Many given things from their parents. Wanting to earn more money and advance quickly. Willing to change jobs to get ahead. Generation /Millennials—Many getting a degree and wanting higher pay and advancement quicker than past. Most likely to change jobs and go with other companies for salary and position advancement (DG001).

Traditionalists believed in following the rules. Baby Boomers work very hard /diligently (DG008). Generation Xers tend to require more tangible benefits like 401k, profit sharing, stock options, and sabbatical time. Generation Y/Millennials tend to be socially conscious and tech savvy (DG006). Traditionalists and Baby Boomers like the satisfaction with a job well done and recognition by peers. Generation Xers are often ambitious and anxious to climb the company ladder (DG015). Millennials are trying to learn the business and how they fit into the company (DG005).

THEME 3: STRESS AMONG THE DIFFERENT GENERATIONS IN THE WORKPLACE

Question 7: *What are some of the things you could learn from the other generations that will make you better at your job?* How the different generations manage the stress in the workplace was the most popular response from the participants. This theme was relevant and consistent to the responses from the participants.

Here are several pertinent quotes:

Traditionalists—It is amazing how Gen Xers and the Millennials handle stress in the workplace without affecting the daily operations of the company. What is their secret (DG003)? Baby Boomers—Today's workplace is very stressful. How do the Gen Xers handle the stress? This generation must be built to handle stress (D006). Gen Xers—I always wonder how the Traditionalists and the Baby Boomers were able to handle their stress, especially when the discussions and situations started to deteriorate (DG011). Millennials—The Traditionalists and Baby Boomers seem to be stressed out during critical situations where decisions have to be made that could affect the performance of the company (DG016).

THEME 4: IMPORTANCE OF DEVELOPING AND SETTING GOALS/OBJECTIVES

Question 16: *Would you elaborate on the importance of your manager and you developing paths to high performance and high rewards for achieving the objective or a goal setting process that will assist you in your career?* The responses from the participants is that all the generations felt that developing and setting career goals/objectives are critical in keeping the generations motivated.

Here are some pertinent quotes:

Traditionalist—It is vital to set measureable goals and objectives for analysis of achievement. If distinct measurement/time lines are not put in place in the beginning, it will be very hard to determine levels of achievement in relation to your goals and objectives, and motivation could be affected (DG004).

Baby Boomer—The goal setting process is crucial to enabling the individual to prioritize among normal daily activities, and maintain a focus on the critical path to success as agreed at the beginning of the cycle. The performance criteria and reward levels provide both parties with the necessary metrics to jointly identify what success looks like at the end of the cycle. Using those two steps for each cycle allows for motivation and cohesiveness for employees (DG008). Gen Xers—To ensure growth, it is always important that every employee gets accessed occasionally to make sure that their performance is aligned properly with the company's expectations. This is not only important to the company but for the individual in terms of performance, motivation, and cohesiveness (DG012). Millennials—This is important to me. Good measuring tools can assist in aligning your targets and goals with the company. This will provide motivation and cohesiveness (DG016).

THEME 5: IDENTIFYING THE BEHAVIOR, DIFFERENT STYLE OF THINKING, AND PERFORMANCE

Question 3: *When you are working with someone from another generation, did you notice a difference in demeanor pertaining to behavior, different style of thinking, and performance that is associated with those specific generations?* This question was to ascertain any knowledge that members of a different generation has about another generation relevant to behavior, style of thinking, and performance.

Here are some of the pertinent quotes:

The Millennials that I work with are intelligent, optimistic, technologically competent/ skilled, and able to do more than one thing at a time. This seems to drive them to succeed at work. I have noticed that they prefer to look up information on the computer than to ask for help from more experienced colleagues. Salary is a strong concern (DG008). Traditionalists are very experienced, loyal, respect authority, and keep the younger people on the straight and narrow in order to keep them off trouble or getting into trouble. The information that they provide are rock steady. One can depend on their advice and guidance (DG014). Baby Boomers that I know and work with are workaholics, competitive, and prefer formal meetings and yearly performance review. Baby Boomers want freedom and independence in making decisions. Baby Boomers want competitive salaries, fancy titles, and recognitions. (DG009) Generation Xers seem to be proficient in utilizing computers and social media applications and independence. They feel that job change is a necessity in building dual career. They are good candidates for leadership advancement, and do not like to be micromanaged. The Millennials seem to have a sense of entitlement (DG002).

THEME 6: GENERATIONS GETTING ALONG WITH EACH OTHER IN THE WORKPLACE

Question 5: *What do you enjoy the most about working with each of the four generations, and what did you like the least about it?* This question

was designed for exploring the attitudes, beliefs, and feelings of the
different generations in order to produce a more harmonized working
relationship. To justify one of the explanations on why Traditionalists
believed in helping the younger people could probably have come
about during World War II when the older soldiers took it upon
themselves to look out for the younger soldiers.

Here are several relevant quotes:

The Traditionalists possessed integrity and core values that
reinforced our complete trust in them. They projected confidence
in their abilities and knowledge. They believed in their love of
country and duty. Their dedication and sacrifice is second to none.
They believed in giving respect and receiving respect. Traditionalists
believed in helping the younger people. The least is, Traditionalists
are always looking over your shoulder. They are too formal (DG012).
I enjoy the Millennials' mutitasking and collaboration abilities. The
Millennials are a social group. The Millennials love to talk with all
people. They believed in respect. Their impatience can send the
wrong signals some time during discussions (DG008). I liked the
Baby Boomers' strong work ethic and competitiveness. I liked their
loyalty to companies. What I liked the least is their inability to relax
(DG002). The desire of Gen Xers' work and family balance and their
independence. Gen Xers' embrace of diversity. The least thing I like
is their unimpressed with authority attitude and beliefs (DG017).

THEME 7: MANAGING THE DIFFERENT GENERATIONS TO WORK EFFECTIVELY AND EFFICIENTLY UTILIZING EXTRINSIC AND INTRINSIC REWARDS

Question 6: *When working with someone from a different generation, which generations do you think preferred the extrinsic or intrinsic
rewards to make them work more effectively and efficiently?* This question is to ascertain the preferred rewards that the different generations' response to motivate them to increase their effectiveness, efficiencies, and efforts.

Here are some pertinent quotes:

Gen Xers are motivated by salary and a work/family balance. They seem to value their free time. They want special benefit packages and advancement to leadership positions (DG016). For the Traditionalists, it is important to tell them how their experiences and knowledge are required, and they can mentor the younger people. They want to feel needed and they still have a value and can make meaningful contributions to the organization. Traditionalists like talking and being around people (DG008). Baby Boomers seem to be driven by competitive salaries, fancy titles, promotions, and office locations. For example, an office with a door or a window with a view. To Baby Boomers, a performance review once a year is sufficient (DG001). The Millennials like good salaries and signing incentives. They enjoy collaboration and meaningful work assignments (DG009).

THEME 8: GOOD PERFORMANCES WILL LEAD TO ATTRACTIVE REWARDS

Question 12: *Do you believe that your effort will lead to a good performance and that good performance will be rewarded and the rewards will be attractive? Please elaborate on your response.* In this question, one of the most difficult thing about motivating members from the different generations is that rewards that are attractive to some members are unattractive to others. For good performance, what awards would be attractive to different generations and what awards would be unattractive for their good performance.

Here are some of the pertinent quotes:

Traditionalists would like to be respected and to be important to the company. They believed that their good performance leads to these rewards. They like award trophies/medals and praise. Medals symbolized honor, dedication, and sacrifice. Also, Traditionalists believed their good performance throughout the years will lead to the company providing them with a retirement package (pension and health benefits) that will take care of them in their golden years. Just the satisfaction of a job well done. At this point, Traditionalists are no longer interested in the great office locations or the fancy titles at the office (DG002). Gen Xers want rewards for their good performances to be compensated accordingly, and promotions. Advancement to management and supervision positions. Gen Xers do not want to be micromanaged (DG013). Baby Boomers feel that their rewards for good performances would be money, fancy titles, and recognition by the managers and supervisors. They do not require frequent feedback (DG005). Millennials want for their good performances good salary and meaningful work. Millennials want to receive praise in front of associates. Millennials do not want to be told to "wait and your time will come" (DG016).

THEME 9: TRANSFORMATIONAL LEADERSHIP CAN PROVIDE MOTIVATION, INSPIRATION, AND COHESIVENESS AMONG THE DIFFERENT GENERATIONS

Question 14: *In working with members from the other generations, would you elaborate that transformational leadership from the perspective motivation and inspiration can bring cohesiveness to people of all generations? For example, somebody like Dr. Martin Luther King, President Kennedy, President Obama or General Colin Powell could provide this transformational leadership?* This question was designed to see how transformational leadership can bring about motivation, inspiration, and cohesiveness among the different generations. Also, this will be an attempt to gain further insight from the different generations on their perspectives.

Some relevant quotes:

Baby Boomers, well, what I saw in Traditionalists were during the late 1970s when the Chrysler Corporation was on the edge of financial upheaval. People were about to lose their jobs and savings and health packages. A man called Mr. Lee Iacocca enters the picture. Mr. Iacocca presented his vision and the mission to the Traditionalist and Baby Boomer employees and was able to rally the majority of the employees behind him to save Chrysler. He projected confidence and a strong personality. Mr. Iacocca's good reputation in the automobile industry is as the man who engineered the Mustang for Ford. He pledged to the employees that his salary as head of Chrysler would be one dollar until the company came out of their financial crisis and commence making profits. He made television and radio commercials about how great the Chrysler automobiles were. If people can find a better automobile, then he suggested that they should buy it. Traditionalists thought that this was brilliant. All of this motivated and brought cohesiveness among the different generations. He was an inspiration (DG005). For the Traditionalists, when President Kennedy presented his vision and mission to NASA for landing a man on the moon and bringing him safely back to Earth before the end of the decade motivated, inspired, and brought cohesiveness among the Traditionalists and Baby Boomers. President Kennedy was a charismatic leader with a dynamic personality that attracted followers. He was optimistic (DG001). As a Gen Xer, there was General Electric in a financial crisis, and along came Mr. Jack Welch, a dynamic leader. He gives his vision and mission to the employees and got the employees to believe in him and to follow him in turning around General Electric. The employees who were Traditionalists, Baby Boomers, and Gen Xers were motivated and inspired. His vision and mission made the different generations want to work together (DG011).

THEME 10: ORGANIZATIONAL CULTURE CAN PROVIDE MOTIVATION, COHESION, AND IMPROVE PERFORMANCE

Question 15: *When working with members from other generations how important is organizational culture?* This question was to determine how important organizational culture is to people for providing motivation, cohesion, and improving performance among the different generations.

Here are several pertinent quotes:

In working with members from the Traditionalists, the company's organizational culture is very important. Organizational culture has an effect on behavior. It establishes the behavior, rewards, and what best practices will be accepted for the organization. The organizational culture can set how you behave, speak, and dress in the workplace. This can bring about motivation and cohesiveness in the workplace among the different generations. This can increase productivity (DG005).

When I was working with the Baby Boomers, I found organizational culture as critical to the company and how people will get along and work together to get an assignment. It can offer inclusionary, therefore creating a strong and cohesive environment (DG002). I noticed with the Millennials that organizational culture was extremely important. Organizational culture can promote cooperative behavior, motivation, performance, and collaboration (DG012). Generation Xers seem to believe that organizational culture is important. Organizational culture can produce standards that control behavior. What one has to do to get along? Effective organizational culture can improve performance and reduce absenteeism (DG016).

THEME 11: THEORIES FOR MANAGING AND MOTIVATING THE FOUR DIFFERENT GENERATIONS

Question 8. *In working with members from other generations, what generations do you believe fit into the following and please elaborate:*

- *Need to be told what to do at work*
- *Need to be watched and micromanaged for their assignments at work*
- *Want to work unsupervised and have the freedom to make decisions at work*
- *Have an aspiration to maintain interpersonal relations with people*
- *Have requirements of affiliation, achievement, and power*
- *Have desires for self-development and personal growth*

Need to be told what to do—This would apply to Gen Xers and Millennials. Because of their over lack of experience (DG014). Need to be watched and micromanaged for their assignments at work—This would apply to the Millennials. Because of their lack of experience (DG003). Want to work unsupervised and freedom to make decisions at work—This would apply to the Traditionalists and Baby Boomers (DG012). Have an aspiration to maintain interpersonal relations with people—This applies to the Millennials. Because they like their socializing in the workplace, and they value collaboration (DG008). Have requirements of affiliation, achievement, and power—This would apply to Gen Xers and Baby Boomers. Also, an esteemed requirement (DG002). Have desire for self–development and personal growth—Gen Xers and Millennials (DG011).

THEME 12: BEHAVIOR IS A FUNCTION OF ITS CONSEQUENCES

Question 13: *In working with other members of a different generation, would you believe that their behavior is a function of its consequences, which means that behaviors followed by positive consequences will occur more frequently than those followed by negative consequences?* This question was designed to show if behavior is a function of its consequences in the workplace.

Here are some pertinent quotes:

Traditionalists believed that if you do a good job, then you will be awarded appropriately. If you are dedicated, follow orders, loyal and respect authority then you will be rewarded (DG005). Baby Boomers feel that if you work very hard and your performance is good, then you will be rewarded. If your performance is bad, then you will not be rewarded (DG009). Gen Xers believed that if your performance is good, then you will be awarded accordingly (DG015). Millennials feel that if they do meaningful work and their performance is good, then they will be awarded (DG009).

THEME 13: STRATEGIES FOR RECRUITING AND RETAINING TALENTED PEOPLE FROM THE FOUR DIFFERENT GENERATIONS

Question 17: *What are your company's strategies for recruiting and retaining talented people from the four different generations?* This question was to ascertain the companies' strategies for recruiting and retaining talented people from the four different generations.

Some pertinent quotes:

My company's strategies for recruiting and retaining talented people from the different generations are offering Baby Boomers, Gen Xers, and Millennials competitive salaries (DG001). My company does not have separate strategies for the different generations. There is one strategy to hire and keep the best. They usually always achieve this through the contracting process. An individual is hired as a contractor for a certain period, and is monitored throughout. If an individual proves to be valuable and talented, then he or she is converted to full-time (DG015). We recruit actively from engineering colleges and technical schools. We do not actively recruit others unless there is a special skill or knowledge or capability. We spend a lot of time and effort trying to develop current employees from various generations (DG008). Right now, my company is in transition after the acquisition of another company. At the present moment, I do not know if our strategies will change. We are using competitive salaries and flex-time and working from home (DG016).

Focus Group

The focus group responses to these questions were echoed, and in some instances, consistent with the responses provided by the individual interviews.

Table 3

Purposeful Sample/Four Different Generations/Genders

Genders	Traditionalists	Baby Boomers	Gen Xers	Millennials
Male	X	X	X	X
Female	X	X	X	X

Table 4

Purposeful Sample/Four Different Generations

Participant Coding	Traditionalists	Baby Boomers	Gen Xers	Millennials
DG001	X			
DG002	X			
DG003	X			
DG004	X			
DG005		X		
DG006		X		
DG007		X		
DG008		X		
DG009			X	
DG010			X	
DG011			X	
DG012			X	
DG013				X
DG014				X
DG015				X
DG016				X

Table 5

Focus Group/Sample

Genders	Traditionalists	Baby Boomers	Gen Xers	Millennials
Male	X	X	X	X
Female	X	X	X	X

Participant Coding	Traditionalists	Baby Boomers	Gen Xers	Millennials
DG017	X			
DG018		X		
DG019			X	
DG020				X

SUMMARY

The findings were provided in this chapter from the interview. The open-ended questions were designed to obtain detailed description information from the research participants pertaining to the phenomenon. The interviewer's questions were structured. The analyzed data form the themes.

CHAPTER 5

SUMMARY, CONCLUSIONS, AND RECOMMENDATIONS

Τhis is the first time in the history of the workplace where you have four different and unique generations coming together in the workplace. The purpose of this study was to investigate how to manage the four different generations in order to increase cohesiveness and motivation in the workplace, and to ascertain which methods, theories, or activities of motivation can be utilized to enhance motivation and cohesiveness among each generation and minimize collisions and clashes in the workplace. Managing the different generations is necessary in order to increase cohesiveness and motivation. Motivating these different generations appropriately could determine the success or failure of the companies. According to Lancaster and Stillman (2005), the ramifications of these conflicts and collisions among the different generations can cause a reduction in profitability, loss of talented employees, higher payroll costs, unsatisfied clients, and serious health issues caused by stress. Motivation to manage how effectively and efficiently the different generations work together to achieve the goals of the organization can be a challenge for contemporary companies.

An article by John Sullivan (n.d.), *Longevity/Older People– Employment/Living and Working Longer,* discussed how, in the United

States, healthier lifestyle living and reduced fertility rates will make the workforce of the future different from the workforce of past generations. More mature workers will work longer for various reasons such as money and mental stimulation, and a younger generation will require more flexible schedules for caring for sick parents and younger children. Individuals from the four generations possess important diverse skill sets and different levels of technological competencies. An article by Sarah Fister Gale (2014), *Bridging the Great Divide,* speaks about the influx of young talented people who have different attitudes about methods of communication and collaboration in performing daily function within the company.

SUMMARY

The research sample included people from each generation and the ages ranged from twenty-two 22- to 69 sixty-nine-years-old people with different backgrounds, educational levels, and disciplines. The focus group was utilized that consisted of people from each generation for gathering data in multiple ways from different sources. Each generation brought their own beliefs, norms, behaviors, culture, and expectations to the workplace. The US Census Bureau's current population survey from 2010, revealed that Traditionalists make up 12.7% of the population which equates to 38,600,000; Baby Boomers consists of 79,800,000 which is 26.2%; Gen Xers make up 19.8%, which is 60,100,000; and the Millennials at 27.5%, which is 83,600,000 (Current Population Survey: 2010, 2011). With the appropriate motivation methods and theories, managers can generate new ideas and voices that present a fresh perspective from the members of each of the four different generations. The two most powerful motivational tools are intrinsic motivation and extrinsic motivation. Managers and supervisors must be aware of the generational differences. Delcampo et al. (2011) stated in their book *Managing the Multi-Generational Workforce* that in order to create a more motivated and cohesive workplace, management must view the generational differences as a strength. Traditionalists, Baby Boomers, Gen Xers, and Millennials have their own characteristics. The Traditionalists are loyal. The Baby Boomers are workaholics. Gen Xers want their independence, and the Millennials are multitaskers who seek constant approval and feedback.

Each generation has their own beliefs, norms, cultures, and behavior. All the generations view situations from their own generational perspectives and experiences, and therefore, those managers who do not learn about the different methods and activities for managing each generation will have difficulty motivating and forming cohesiveness with different generations. Motivation can aid the different generations by getting them over the hurdles and bumps placed in their path by management who did not understand the differences between generations. With the increase in life expectancies and the financial need to supplement their retirement, some Baby Boomers will continue to work. Some Traditionalists will come back to work to fulfill their need to be around and interact with people, as well as to supplement their retirement income. This seems to be motivation for them. Gravetta and Throckmorton (2007) explained the unique perspectives and experiences each generation brings to the workforce and how generational management needs to tap into the energy of generational talent by bringing together generations with different motivational needs, perceptions, and behavior styles. Transformational leadership and positive organizational culture can provide motivation and cohesiveness among the different generations in the workplace.

Problem Background

The four different generations in the workplace can create challenges and conflicts for managers and supervisors who must deal with competing priorities, agenda, and values. Having these four different generations in the workplace will create conflicts and collision in the workplace. Lancaster and Stillman (2005) believed that collisions in the workplace happen when two generations bump into each other over just about anything in terms of process, procedures, policies, lack of cohesiveness, motivation, and the organization's culture. For example, cultures can clash when methods and work ethics differ from one generation to the next. All the generations view situations from their own generational perspectives and experiences, and therefore, those managers who do not investigate different methods and activities for managing each generation are having difficulty motivating and forming cohesiveness with different generation. Managers and supervisors are not getting the most out of the different generations in terms of efforts, effectiveness, and performances because they do not know of the different motivation and cohesiveness concepts, theories, and strategies. It is critical that companies realize this, so a more customized plan for managing the different generations can be assembled.

Management that fails in investigating different motivation and cohesiveness theories, methods, and activities for managing each generation could increase the turnover rate of good and talented employees. The costs associated with high turnover are recruiting, hiring, and training new employees. With high turnover comes a decrease in productivity, efficiency, creativity, and innovation. According to Lancaster and Stillman (2005), these are the tangible and intangible costs of company turnover.

Management's style will have to change and evolve if it is to manage the generations in a way that increases cohesiveness and motivation. Motivating and engaging the different generations can contribute positive impacts to companies and their internal organizations.

The literature review provided the information about the different characteristics between the four generations in the workplace. The literature also provided theories and methods that can be utilized to increase motivation and cohesiveness among the four different generations in the workplace. Members of each generation are motivated differently. The literature review contained information that explained why one motivation and cohesiveness method will not work to achieve the desired results from Traditionalists, Baby Boomers, Gen Xers, and Millennials. The literature review provided an understanding as to why such differences exist between the generations. However, this does not mean that one generation is better than the others. There are some books and articles dealing with the phenomenon of four different generations in the workplace from motivational and leadership aspects.

Chapter three deals with why the researcher decided to utilize this research method in studying the chosen phenomena. Based on the phenomena that have been identified, it was best to research utilizing the qualitative methodologies in conjunction with the phenomenological approach for this research design study. Pure phenomenological research seeks to describe rather than explain, and to commence from a perspective free from hypotheses or preconceptions (Husserl, 1970). The phenomenological purpose is to gather detailed descriptions and understand a specific phenomenon. This chapter defines the methodology that was utilized in the research study. Also, the researcher acknowledges his bias in the study being from the Baby Boomer generation.

Chapter four speaks about research design, population, sample, participants, qualitative data collections, validity, data analysis, and findings. During the interview, open-ended questions were provided to the research participants. This way, the researcher was able to obtain the views, opinions, and more detailed information from the participants. The researcher utilized the convenience sampling method. Participants were easily recruited and accessible. This method was quick and inexpensive. The population of this study came from four different generations. The qualitative research collected and gathered information from the chosen participants through interviews. The participant's ages ranged from twenty-two-year-olds to sixty-nine-year-olds. The participants were males and females with different backgrounds and years of education.

THEMES DEVELOPED FROM RESEARCH

After analyzing, evaluating, and interpreting the responses provided by the research participants, the following themes and trends emerged.

THEME 1: MOTIVATION AND COHESIVENESS FACTOR FOR EACH GENERATION

The responses by the research participants revealed that each generation had different motivations and cohesiveness factors that contributed to their performances and togetherness in terms of economic incentives, recognition, praise, and achieving objectives. These extrinsic and intrinsic rewards seem to generate the theme. This theme was consistent with most of the responses.

Participant DG004 stated,

"A combination of all the things mentioned in question four."

Participant DG006 stated,

"Baby Boomers are motivated by salary, formal meetings, and competition."

Participant DG010 stated,

"Gen Xers want to be compensated sufficiently for their performances."

Participant DG012 stated,

"Millennials: The latest technological tools for them to do their work. Good salaries and flexible work environment."

THEME 2: DIFFERENT CHARACTERISTICS OF THE FOUR DIFFERENT GENERATIONS

The responses showed that participants were aware of a couple of the different characteristics of the four generations. This theme was consistent with most of the responses.

Here are a few of the research participant quotes:

According to Participant DG001,

"Traditionalists: Glad to have a job and work hard. Would retire with the same company. Baby Boomers: Many went to college to get a degree and a good job. Work hard to get ahead. Likely to retire with the same company. Gen Xers: Many getting a degree. Many given things from their parents. Wanting to earn more money and advance quickly. Willing to change jobs to get ahead. Millennials: Many getting a degree and wanting higher pay and advancement quicker than past. Most likely to change jobs and go with other companies for salary and position advancement."

Participant DG008 stated,

"Traditionalists believed in following the rules. Baby Boomers work very hard/diligently."

Participant DG006 stated,

"Generation Xers tend to require more tangible benefits such as 401k, profit sharing, stock options, and sabbatical time. Generation Y/Millennials tend to be socially conscious and tech savvy."

Participant DG015 stated,

"Traditionalists and Baby Boomers like the satisfaction of a job well done and recognition by peers. Generation Xers are often ambitious and anxious to climb the company ladder."

Participant DG005 stated,

"Millennials are trying to learn the business and how they fit into the company."

THEME 3: STRESS AMONG THE DIFFERENT GENERATIONS IN THE WORKPLACE

How the different generations manage the stress in the workplace was the most popular response from the participants. This theme was relevant and consistent to the response from the participants.

Participant DG003 stated,

"Traditionalists: It is amazing how Gen Xers and the Millennials handle stress in the workplace without affecting the daily operations of the company. What is their secret?"

Participant DG006 stated,

"Baby Boomers: Today's workplace is very stressful. How do the Gen Xers handle the stress? This generation must be built to handle stress."

Participant DG011 stated,

"Gen Xers: I always wonder how the Traditionalists and the Baby Boomers were able to handle their stress, especially when the discussions and situations started to deteriorate."

Participant DG016 stated,

"Millennials: The Traditionalists and Baby Boomers seem to be stressed out during critical situations where decisions have to be made that could affect the performance of the company."

THEME 4: IMPORTANCE OF DEVELOPING AND SETTING GOALS/OBJECTIVES

The responses from the participants are that all the generations felt that developing and setting career goals/objectives are critical in keeping the generations motivated.

Participant DG004 stated,

"Traditionalist: It is vital to set measureable goals and objectives for analysis of achievement. If distinct measurement/time lines are not put in place in the beginning, it will be very hard to determine levels of achievement in relation to your goals and objectives, and motivation could be affected."

Participant DG008 stated,

"Baby Boomer: The goal setting process is crucial to enabling the individual to prioritize among normal daily activities, and maintain a focus on the critical path to success as agreed at the beginning of the cycle. The performance criteria and reward levels provide both parties with the necessary metrics to jointly identify what success looks like at the end of the cycle. Using those two steps for each cycle allows for motivation and cohesiveness for employees."

Participant DG012 stated,

"Gen Xers: To ensure growth, it is always important that every employee gets assessed occasionally to make sure that their performance is aligned properly with the company's expectations. This is not only important to the company but for the individual in terms of performance, motivation, and cohesiveness."

Participant DG016 stated,

"Millennials: This is important to me. Good measuring tools can assist in aligning your targets and goals with the company. This will provide motivation and cohesiveness."

THEME 5: IDENTIFYING THE BEHAVIOR, DIFFERENT STYLE OF THINKING, AND PERFORMANCE

This question was to ascertain any knowledge that members of a different generation have about another generation relevant to behavior, style of thinking, and performance.

Some of the research participant quotes are as follows:

Participant DG008 stated,

"The Millennials that I work with are intelligent, optimistic, technologically competent/skilled, and able to do more than one thing at a time. This seems to drive them to succeed at work. I have noticed that they prefer to look up information on the computer than to ask for help from more experienced colleagues. Salary is a strong concern."

Participant DG014 stated,

"Traditionalists are very experienced, loyal, respect authority, and keep the younger people on the straight and narrow in order to keep them out of trouble or from getting into trouble. The information that they provide is rock steady. One can depend on their advice and guidance."

Participant DG009 stated,

"Baby Boomers that I know and work with are workaholics, competitive, and prefer formal meetings and yearly performance reviews. Baby Boomers want freedom and independence in making decisions. Baby Boomers want competitive salaries, fancy titles, and recognitions."

Participant DG002 stated,

"Generation Xers seem to be proficient in utilizing computers and social media applications and independence. They feel that job change is a necessity in building a dual career. They are good candidates for leadership advancement, and do not like to be micromanaged. The Millennials seem to have a sense of entitlement."

Theme 6: Generations Getting Along with Each Other in the Workplace

This question was designed for exploring the attitudes, beliefs, and feelings of the different generations in order to produce a more harmonized working relationship. To justify one of the explanations on why Traditionalists believed in helping the younger people could probably have come about during World War II when the older soldiers took it upon themselves to look out for the younger soldiers.

Some research participant's relevant quotes are as follows:

According to Participant DG012:

"The Traditionalists possessed integrity and core values that reinforced our complete trust in them. They projected confidence in their abilities and knowledge. They believed in their love of country and duty. Their dedication and sacrifice is second to none. They believed in giving respect and receiving respect. Traditionalists believed in helping the younger people. The least is, Traditionalists are always looking over your shoulder. They are too formal."

Participant DG008 stated,

"I enjoy the Millennials' mutitasking and collaboration abilities. The Millennials are a social group. The Millennials love to talk with all people. They believed in respect. Their impatience can send the wrong signals some time during discussions."

Participant DG002 stated,

"I liked the Baby Boomers' strong work ethic and competitiveness. I liked their loyalty to companies. What I liked the least is their inability to relax."

Participant DG017 stated,

"The desire of Gen Xers for work and family balance and their independence. Gen Xers embrace diversity. The least thing I like is, they are unimpressed with authority attitude and beliefs."

THEME 7: MANAGING THE DIFFERENT GENERATIONS TO WORK EFFECTIVELY AND EFFICIENTLY UTILIZING EXTRINSIC AND INTRINSIC REWARDS

This question is to ascertain the preferred rewards that the different generations responded to as to what motivates them to increase their effectiveness, efficiencies, and efforts.

Participant DG016 stated,

"Gen Xers are motivated by salary and a work/family balance. They seem to value their free time. They want special benefit packages and advancement to leadership positions."

Participant DG008 stated,

"For the Traditionalists, it is important to tell them how their experiences and knowledge are required, and they can mentor the younger people. They want to feel needed and they still have a value and can make meaningful contributions to the organization. Traditionalists like talking and being around people."

Participant DG001 stated,

"Baby Boomers seem to be driven by competitive salaries, fancy titles, promotions, and office locations. For example, an office with a door or a window with a view. To Baby Boomers, a performance review once a year is sufficient."

Participant DG009 stated,

"The Millennials like good salaries and signing incentives. They enjoy collaboration and meaningful work assignments."

THEME 8: GOOD PERFORMANCES WILL LEAD TO ATTRACTIVE REWARDS

In this question, one of the most difficult thing about motivating members from the different generations is that rewards that are attractive to some members are unattractive to others. For good performance, what awards would be attractive to different generations and what awards would be unattractive for their good performance.

Participant DG002 stated,

"Traditionalists would like to be respected and to be important to the company. They believed that their good performance leads to these rewards. They like award trophies/medals and praise. Medals symbolized honor, dedication, and sacrifice. Also, Traditionalists believed their good performance throughout the years will lead to the company providing them with a retirement package (pension and health benefits) that will take care of them in their golden years. Just the satisfaction of a job well done. At this point, Traditionalists are no longer interested in the great office locations or the fancy titles at the office."

Participant DG013 stated,

"Gen Xers want rewards for their good performances to be compensated accordingly, and promotions. Advancement to management and supervision positions. Gen Xers do not want to be micromanaged."

Participant DG005 stated,

"Baby Boomers feel that their rewards for good performances would be money, fancy titles, and recognition by the managers and supervisors. They do not require frequent feedback."

Participant DG016 stated,

"Millennials want for their good performances good salary and meaningful work. Millennials want to receive praise in front of associates. Millennials do not want to be told to 'wait and your time will come.'"

THEME 9: TRANSFORMATIONAL LEADERSHIP CAN PROVIDE MOTIVATION, INSPIRATION, AND COHESIVENESS AMONG THE DIFFERENT GENERATIONS

This question was designed to see how transformational leadership can bring about motivation, inspiration, and cohesiveness among the different generations. Also, this was an attempt to gain further insight from the different generations on their perspectives.

Participant DG005 stated,

"Well, what I saw in Traditionalists were during the late 1970s when the Chrysler Corporation was on the edge of financial upheaval. People were about to lose their jobs and savings and health packages. A man called Mr. Lee Iacocca enters the picture. Mr. Iacocca presented his vision and the mission to the Traditionalist and Baby Boomer employees and was able to rally the majority of the employees behind him to save Chrysler. He projected confidence and a strong personality. Mr. Iacocca's good reputation in the automobile industry was as the man who engineered the Mustang for Ford. He pledged to the employees that his salary as head of Chrysler would be one dollar until the company came out of their financial crisis and commence making profits. He made television and radio commercials about how great the Chrysler automobiles were. If people can find a better automobile, then he suggested that they should buy it. Traditionalists

thought that this was brilliant. All of this motivated and brought cohesiveness among the different generations. He was an inspiration."

Participant DG001 stated,

"For the Traditionalists, when President Kennedy
presented his vision and mission to NASA for
landing a man on the moon and bringing him
safely back to Earth before the end of the decade
motivated, inspired, and brought cohesiveness
among the Traditionalists and Baby Boomers.
President Kennedy was a charismatic leader with
a dynamic personality that attracted followers.
He was optimistic."

Participant DG011 stated,

"As a Gen Xer, there was General Electric in a
financial crisis and along came Mr. Jack Welch,
a dynamic leader. He gives his vision and mission to the employees and got the employees
to believe in him and to follow him in turning
around General Electric. The employees from
the Traditionalists, Baby Boomers, and Gen–
Xers were motivated and inspired. His vision and
mission made the different generations want to
work together."

THEME 10: ORGANIZATIONAL CULTURE CAN PROVIDE MOTIVATION, COHESION, AND IMPROVE PERFORMANCE

This question was to determine how important organizational culture is to people for providing motivation, cohesion, and improvement in performance among the different generations. According to

PM Network, October 2014, culture is critical when top management is involved with value requirements. A majority of participants believed that positive organizational culture was critical and important for companies.

Participant DG005 stated,

"In working with members from the Traditionalists, the company's organizational culture is very important. Organizational culture has an effect on behavior. It establishes the behavior, rewards, and what best practices will be accepted for the organization. The organizational culture can set how you behave, speak, and dress in the workplace. This can bring about motivation and cohesiveness in the workplace among the different generations. This can increase productivity."

Participant DG002 stated,

"When I was working with the Baby Boomers, I found organizational culture to be critical to the company and how people will get along and work together to get assignment. It can offer inclusionary, therefore creating a strong and cohesive environment."

Participant DG012 stated,

"I noticed with the Millennials that organizational culture was extremely important. Organizational culture can promote cooperative behavior, motivation, performance, and collaboration."

Participant DG016 stated,

"Generation Xers seem to believe that organizational culture is important. Organizational culture can produce standards that control behavior. What one has to do to get along? Effective organizational culture can improve performance and reduce absenteeism."

THEME 11: THEORIES FOR MANAGING AND MOTIVATING THE FOUR DIFFERENT GENERATIONS

This question was designed to find out what theories could be used effectively to manage and motivate members from four different generations. Based on the responses from the participants, the McGregor Theory X and Theory Y, McClelland's Learned Needs, and Maslow's Hierarchy would be the theories that would assist in managing and motivating members from the four different generations. In certain situations, the blending of all the theories mentioned above could produce the desired results.

Participant DG014 stated,

"Need to be told what to do. This would apply to Gen Xers and Millennials because of their over lack of experience."

Participant DG003 stated,

"Need to be watched and micromanaged for their assignments at work. This would apply to the Millennials because of their lack of experience."

Participant DG012 stated,

"Want to work unsupervised and freedom to make decisions at work. This would apply to the Traditionalists and Baby Boomers."

Participant DG008 stated,

"Have an aspiration to maintain interpersonal relations with people. This applies to the Millennials. Because they like their socializing in the workplace and they value collaboration."

Participant DG002 stated,

"Have requirements of affiliation, achievement, and power. This would apply to Gen Xers and Baby Boomers. Also, an esteem requirement."

Participant DG011 stated,

"Have desire for self-development and personal growth—Gen Xers and Millennials."

THEME 12: BEHAVIOR IS A FUNCTION OF ITS CONSEQUENCES

This question was designed to show if behavior is a function of its consequences in the workplace. The responses from the majority of participants were that if an individual did a good job, then they would be rewarded. If you did a bad job, then you would not be rewarded.

According to Participant DG005, Traditionalists believe that if you do a good job, then you will be rewarded appropriately. If you are dedicated, follow orders, are loyal, and respect authority, then you will be rewarded. Participant DG009 thinks that Baby Boomers feel that if you work very hard and your performance is good, then you will be rewarded. If your performance is bad, then you will not be rewarded. Participant DG015 feels that Gen Xers believed that if your performance is good, then you will be awarded accordingly. Participant DG009 thinks that Millennials feel that if they do meaningful work and their performance is good, then they will be rewarded.

THEME 13: STRATEGIES FOR RECRUITING AND RETAINING TALENTED PEOPLE FROM THE FOUR DIFFERENT GENERATIONS

This question was to ascertain the companies' strategies for recruiting and retaining talented people from the four different generations. Each research participant's company has a different strategy for recruiting and retaining talented people. It seems that their strategies do not suffice when it comes to recruiting talented people from the different generations. Some superficial efforts seem to be made, but they do not go deep enough.

Participant DG001 stated,

"My company's strategies for recruiting and retaining talented people from the different generations are offering Baby Boomers, Gen Xers, and Millennials competitive salaries."

Participant DG015 stated,

"My company does not have separate strategies for the different generations. There is one strategy to hire and keep the best. They usually always achieve this through the contracting process. An individual is hired as a contractor for a certain period and is monitored throughout. If an individual proves to be valuable and talented, then he or she is converted to full-time."

Participant DG008 stated,

"We recruit actively from engineering colleges and technical schools. We do not actively recruit others unless there is a special skill or knowledge or capability. We spend a lot of time and effort trying to develop current employees from various generations."

Participant DG016 stated,

"Right now, my company is in transition after the acquisition of another company. At the present moment, I do not know if our strategies will change. We are using competitive salaries and flex-time and working from home."

Conclusions

Training for motivation about the awareness of the different generations' characteristics and their motivation and cohesiveness are driving factors for performances. This will change their ways of thinking. Each manager and supervisor should be aware of these driving factors so that they can get their subordinates from different generations motivated for their optimal performance. The motivation for these managers and supervisors will be their subordinates' increase in motivation, cohesiveness, and performances which will definitely catch the attention of their upper management. Do not wait for human resources to provide all the answers. However, human resources should provide the training. This will lead to new opportunities for them.

Managers and supervisors should identify the motivation and cohesiveness factors of each member of the generation that are working for them. They should speak to each member of those generations to ascertain motivation and cohesiveness divides. Then, they should utilize this knowledge to build a bridge between the differences that will construct stronger working relationships and dynamics among the different generations. Managers and supervisors should be able to anticipate the challenges and special considerations in managing the different generations involved in conflicts and collisions.

The organization's culture can be a key factor in creating motivation and cohesiveness. According to Marcus (2011), cultures can be weak or strong because of attributes, attitudes, professionalism, achievement orientation, certain amount of autonomy, compensation equity, and moral and ethical integrity. The organization's culture can be linked to shared values where there is unity of purpose because of culture and a common vision to take the company to where it should be heading (Marcus, 2011, p. 59). This can bring people together rather than separating them. Companies can create a special culture to get people involved by having a selective hiring process, training, and specific measure of autonomy (Marcus, 2011, p. 71).

The ability to motivate people from the four different generations will become critically important. This is why motivational and cohesiveness strategies that are effective will bring about innovation and creativity to the workplace. The managers and supervisors who can understand, communicate, and motivate these people from the different generations will become a valued resource where upper management will take notice. Understanding the characteristics of the different generations is not just good business practice, but also it is a key to competing successfully for the company.

IMPLICATIONS FOR PRACTICE

There are key factors to successfully managing the different generations in order to increase motivation and cohesiveness. Managers and supervisors' abilities to manage the different generations can be challenging when there are competing priorities, agenda, cultures, behaviors, norms, and values. Managers and supervisors are not getting the most effort and performance of the different generations because they do not know of the different motivation and cohesiveness concepts, theories, and strategies. Managing subordinates in a multigenerational environment could be challenging. However, through awareness and acceptance of generational differences, the organization will take off.

RECOMMENDATIONS

Some of the recommendations for managing the different generations in order to achieve success are as follows:

1. Establish mentoring programs where members of one generation can mentor the others. This will build new skill sets and lasting professional relationships.
2. Encourage older and retiring employees to transfer knowledge to younger and new employees.
3. Companies should form a program for interns and not just college millennials but all millennials who want to learn a profession. All companies should be trying to reach out to millennials if the companies want to increase revenues and profits. It will be imperative that companies reach out to millennials if they want to maintain innovation, collaboration, sustainability and survive.
4. Utilize motivational and cohesiveness factors that contributed to the different generations' performance and togetherness in terms of economic incentives, recognition, and praise.
5. Utilize a blend of the McGregor's Theory X and Theory Y, Maslow's Hierarchy, McClelland's Learned Needs, Alderfer's ERG Theory, Equity Theory, Expectancy Theory, and the Reinforcement Theory.
6. Articulate clear and precise vision and mission for the organization.

7. Ensure that positive and powerful organizational cultures are in the workplace.

8. Get out of your comfort zone. Take on a different way of doing work. For example, embracing technology if you prefer doing things in person. Face-to-face communication if you prefer technology.

9. Perform a personal SWOT (strengths, weaknesses, opportunities, and threats) analysis that will produce ideas that will promote generational motivation, cohesiveness, and collaboration.

10. Promote core values.

11. Reward collaborative contributions and teamwork (Tucker, Kao, and Verma, 2005).

12. Stress the commonalities among the different generations such as the need to earn a living and interacting with colleagues and performing meaningful assignments.

13. Promote generational engagement. When engaged means that the individual is consistently seeking excellence and is motivated by the work (MetLife Mature Market Institute, 2009).

14. Provide constructive feedback that motivates and obtains results so that a person leaves with a sense of fairness during the performance review. Increasing revenue and reducing cost doesn't have to be exclusive for larger corporations. Small business can benefit from this information as well.

Helpful Equations in Managing the Different Generations

Critical Thinking + Commitment + Collaboration + Confidence + Cohesiveness + Courtesy = Successful Performance. This equation is called The Six (6) Cs. Good Preparation + Good Planning + Motivation + Innovation + Good Performance = Success

Based on the interview analysis, themes, theories, patterns, interpretations, and the implications of this research indicated that each generation has knowledge of some of the other characteristics that could be helpful when working with each other in today workplace.

LIST OF TABLES

———⟨≡⟩———

REFERENCES

—⊂▦⊃—

Adams, R. L. (2013). *How not to give up: A motivational and inspirational guide to goal setting and achieving your dreams.* CreateSpace Independent Publishing Platform.

Asplund, J., and Blacksmith, N. (2012, March). Strength-Based Goal Setting. *Gallup Business Journal.* Retrieved February 18, 2013, from http://businessjournal.gallup.com/content/152981strengths-based-goal-setting.aspx

Bainbridge, S. M. (2007). The Complete Guide to Sarbanes-Oxley. *The Complete Guide to Sarbanes-Oxley, Adams Business,* 07–17.

Barnes, J. A. (2005). *John F. Kennedy on leadership: The lessons and legacy of a president.* New York: AMACOM.

Bates, S. (2008). *Motivate like a CEO: Communicate your strategic vision and inspire people to act.* New York: McGraw-Hill.

Bennett, D. (2009, March 15). Ready, aim….fail. Why setting goals can backfire. The Boston Globe, C1.

Benson, J. D. (2008). Leadership and motivation. Retrieved from EBSCO Research Starters.

Brokaw, T. (1998). *The greatest generation.* Random House LLC.

Brown, L.V. (2007). *Psychology of motivation.* New York: Nova Science Publishers.

Bureau of Labor Statistics. (n.d.). Retrieved from http://wwwbls.gov/news-releaseljolts.nro.ntm

Bush, G. W. (2010). *Decision points.* New York: Crown.

Cameron, K. S., and Quinn, R. E. (2011). *Diagnosing and changing organizational culture: Based on the competing values framework.* John Wiley and Sons.

Collis, D. J., and Montgomery, C. A. (2008). Competing on resources. *Harvard Business Review.*

Cone, J. D., and Foster, S. L. (1993). *Dissertations and theses from start to finish.* Washington, DC: American Psychological Association.

Conger, J. A. (1999). Charismatic and transformational leadership in organizations: An insider's perspective on these developing streams of research. *The Leadership Quarterly, 10*(2), 145–179.

Conley, C. (2007). *PEAK: How great companies get their mojo from Maslow* (Vol. 263). San Francisco, CA: Jossey-Bass.

Coon, D., and Mitterer, J. O. (2010). *Introduction to psychology: Gateways to mind and behavior with concept maps.* Belmont, CA: Wadsworth

Corker, K. S., and Donnellan, M. B. (2012). Setting lower limits high: The role of boundary goals in achievement motivation. *Journal of Educational Psychology, 104*(1), 138–149. doi: 10.1037/a0026228.

Creswell, J. W. (2009). *Research design qualitative, quantitative, and mixed methods approaches.* Los Angeles, CA: Sage.

Current Population Survey: 2010. (2011). United States Census Bureau. *Newsroom Archive*. Retrieved from https://www.census.gov/newsroom/releases/archives/population/cb11-tps16.html

Davila, T., Epstein, M. J., and Shelton, R. D. (2006). *The Creative Enterprise* [Three Volumes]. Greenwood Publishing Group.

Deal, J. J., Stawiski, S., Graves, L., Gentry, W. A., Weber, T. J., and Ruderman, M. (2013). Motivation at work: Which matters more, generation or managerial level? *Consulting Psychology Journal, Practice and Research, 65*(1), 1.

DelCampo, M. R. G., Haney, M. J., Haggerty, L. A., and Knippel, L. A. (2012). *Managing the multi-generational workforce: From the GI generation to the millennials*. Gower Publishing, Ltd.

Dickinson, A. M., and Poling, A. D. (1996). Schedules of monetary reinforcement in organizational behavior management: Latham and Huber (1992) revisited. *Journal of Organizational Behavior Management, 16*(1), 71–91.

Drucker, P. F. (2007). *Managing in the next society*. Routledge.

Erickson, T. (2008). *Plugged in: The generation Y guide to thriving at work*. Harvard Business Review Press.

Gale, S. F. (2014). Bridging the great divides. Retrieved from http://marketplace.pmi.org/Pages/ProductDetail.aspx?GMProduct=00101359300

Gergen, C., and Vanourek, G. (2009, January 14). Properly set goals aid success. *The Washington Times, B03*.

Gilman, H. (2011). *You can't fire everyone: And other lessons from an accidental manager*. New York, NY: Penguin Group.

Gordinier, J. (2008). X Saves the World: *How Generation X Got the Shaft But Can Still Keep Everything from Sucking*. New York, NY: Penguin Group.

Gravetta, T., and Throckmorthon, R. (2007). *Bridging the Generation Gap: How to get radio babies, boomers, Gen Xers, and Gen Yers to work together and achieve more*. Career Press.

Green, T. (2000). *Motivation management: Fueling performance by discovering what people believe about themselves and their organizations*. Palo Alto, CA: Davies-Black.

Griggs, R. A. (2010). *Psychology: A concise introduction*. New York, NY: Worth.

Hall, J. (2007). Understanding employees is a generational thing. *Air Conditioning Heating and Refrigeration New, 230*(10), 22.

Halvorson, H, G. (2010). *Succeed: How we can reach our goals*. New York, NY: Penguin.

Hesselbein, F., Goldsmith, M., and Somerville, I. (2002). *Leading for innovation and organizing for results*. San Francisco: Jossey-Bass.

Horn, T. S. (2008). *Advances in sport psychology*. Champaign, IL: Human Kinetics.

House, R. J. (1971). A path goal theory of leader effectiveness. *Administrative Science Quarterly*, 321–339.

House, R. J., and Mitchell, T. R. (1974). Path-goal theory of leadership. *Journal of Contemporary Business, 3*(4), 81.

Husserl, E. (1970). *The crisis of European sciences and transcendental phenomenology: An introduction to phenomenological philosophy*. Northwestern University Press.

Jeffrey, S. A. (2009). Justifiability and the motivational power of tangible noncash incentives. *Human Performance 22*, 143–155.

Kerry, D. S., and Armour, K. M. (2000). Sport sciences and the promise of phenomenology: Philosophy, method, and insight. *Quest, 52*(1), 1–17.

Kian, T. S., Yusoff, W. F. W., and Rajah, S. (2013). Relationship between motivations and citizenship performance among Generation X and Generation Y. *International Journal of Academic Research in Business and Social Sciences, 3*(11).

Kim, C. W., and Mauborgne, R. (2004). *Blue Ocean Strategy. If you read nothing else on strategy, read these best-selling articles.* Harvard Business School Press, Boston, MA.

King, A., Oliver, B., and Sloop, B. (1995). Planning and Goal Setting for Improved Performance Participants Guide (Performance through participation). Cincinnati, OH: Thomson Executive Press.

Kouzes, J. M., and Posner, B. Z. (2010). *The five practices of exemplary leadership* (Vol. 237). Upper Saddle River, NJ: John Wiley and Sons.

Kuli, A. G. (1992). *The Spirit Descends: A Social History of the Blues* (Doctoral dissertation, Amherst College).

Lancaster, L. C., and Stillman, D. (2005). When generations collide. Who they are. Why they clash. How to solve the generational puzzle at work. *The Management Forum Series.*

Latham, G. P., and Locke, E. A. (2006). Enhancing the benefits and overcoming the pitfalls of goal setting. *Organizational Dynamics, 35*(4), 332–340.

Lawler, E., Porter, L., and Vroom, V. (2009). Motivation and management Vroom's Expectancy Theory. *Value Based Management Website.*

LoBiondo-Wood, G., Haber, J., and Krainovich-Miller, B. (2006). The research process: Integrating evidence-based practice. In G. LoBiondo-Wood, and J. Haber (Eds.), *Nursing research: Methods and critical appraisal for evidence-based practice,* (pp. 27-45). St. Louis: Mosby Elsevier.

Locke, L. F., Spirduso, W. W., and Silverman, S. J. (2007). *Proposals that work: A guide for planning dissertations and grant proposals* (5th ed.). Thousand Oaks, CA: Sage.

Loehr, A., and Kaye, J. (2011). *Managing the unmanageable: How to motivate even the most unruly employee.* Pompton Plains, NJ: The Career Press.

Luthans, F., and Stajkovic, A. D. (1999). Reinforce for performance: The need to go beyond pay and even rewards. *The academy of management executive, 13*(2), 49–57.

Madjar, I., and Walton, J. A. (Eds.). (1999). *Nursing and the experience of illness: Phenomenology in practice.* Psychology Press.

Marcus, A. A. (2011). Management strategy. Achieving sustained competitive advantage. New York, NY: McGraw-Hill Irwin.

Marshall, J. (2004). Managing different generations at work. *Financial Executive, 20*(5), 18–19.

Marston, C. (2007). Retaining Younger Workers in the Workplace. *FastCompany. com, 96.*

Maslow, A. H. (1970). *Motivation and personality* (Vol. 2). New York: Harper and Row.

Maslow, A. H. (2011). *Hierarchy of Needs: A Theory of Human Motivation* (Kindle ed.). Kindle.

McChesney, C., Covey, S., and Huling, J. (2012). The four disciplines of execution. *Franklin Covey, West Valley City, UT.*

MetLife Mature Market Institute. (2009). The Sloan Center on aging and work at Boston College. *The Center on Aging Work.* Retrieved from http://www.bc.edu /research/agingandwork/ archive_news/2009.html

Miner, J. B. (2007). *Organizational behavior 4: From theory to practice.* Armonk, NY: ME Sharp Vance.

Moustakas, C. (1994). *Phenomenological research methods.* Thousand Oaks, CA: Sage.

Mulcahy, R. (2002). *PMP Exam Prep.* RCM Publications.

Murphy, E. F., Gibson, J. W., and Greenwood, R. A. (2010). Analyzing generational values among managers and non–managers for sustainable organizational effectiveness. *SAM Advance Management Journal, 75*(1), 33–55

Myers, D. (2005). *Exploring psychology* (6th ed.). New York: Worth.

Nieswiadomy, M., and Cobb, S. L. (1993). Impact of pricing structure selectivity on urban water demand. *Contemporary Economic Policy, 11*(3), 101–113.

Osterloh, M., and Frey, B. S. (2000). Motivation, knowledge transfer, and organizational forms. *Organization Science, 11*(5), 538-550.

Powell, C., and Koltz, T. (2012). *It Worked For Me: In Life and Leadership.* HarperCollins.

Presslee, A., Vance, T. W., and Webb, R. A. (2013). The effects of reward type on employee goal setting, goal commitment, and performance. *The Accounting Review, 88*(5), 1805–1831.

Project Management Institute. (2013). *Managing Change in Organization: A practice guide.* Retrieved from http://www.pmi. org/Learning/change-management/change-management-form. aspx

Project Management Talent Gap Report. (2014). Retrieved from http://www.pmi.org/knowledge-center/pulse/~/media/pdf-Business-solutions /pmiprojectmanagmentskillsgapreport.ashx

Raghupathy, S. (2010). Title statement: From boomers to bloggers challengers of managing multi–generational team. *Journal Article: PMI Global Congress 2010—Asia Pacific.*

Rajah, S. (2013). Relationship between motivation and citizenship performance among Generation X and Generation Y. *International Journal of Academic Research in Business and Social Sciences, 3*(11).

Saraswathi, S. (2011). A study on factors that motivate IT and non–IT sector employees: A comparsion. *International Journal of Research in Computer Application and Management, 1*(2), 72-77

Shaw, H. (2013). *Sticking points: How to get 4 generations working together.* Carol Stream, Ill: Tyndale House.

Sky Delta Magazine June 2017 Edition, page 11/June 2017 Issue Digital Edition, page 11.

Stein, J. (2013). Millennials: The Me, Me, Me Generation. *Time.*

Steinhorn, L. (2006). *The Greater Generation: In defense of the baby boomer legacy*. Mcmillan.

Stevenson, B., and Wolfers, J. (2007). *Marriage and divorce: Changes and their driving forces* (No. w12944). National Bureau of Economic Research.

Straker, D. (2010). *Changing minds-in detail*. Syque Publ. Retrieved from http: //changingminds.org/explanations/theories /extrinsic_motivation.htm

Sullivan, J. (n.d.). The longevity/older people–employment/ living. Retrieved from http://marketplace.pmi.org/Pages/ ProductDetail.aspx?GMProduct=00100901700

Toossi, M. (2002). Century of change: The US Labor Force, 1950–2050. *Monthly Lab. Rev.*, *125*, 15.

Toossi, M. (2005). Labor force projections to 2014: Retiring boomers. *Monthly Lab. Rev.*, *128*, 25.

Tucker, E., Kao, T., and Verma, N. (2005). Next-Generation Talent Management. *Business Credit*, *107*, 20-27.

Twenge, J. M. (2006). Generation Me: Why today's young Americans are more confident, assertice, entitled—and more miserable than ever before. New York, N.Y: Simon and Schuster.

US Bureau of Labor Statistics. (n.d.). Retrieved from http://www.bls. gov/home.htm

White, B. J., and Prywes, Y. (2007). *The nature of leadership: reptiles, mammals, and the challenge of becoming a great leader*. AMACOM Div American Mgmt Assn.

Wlodkowski, R. J. (1999). *Enhancing adult motivation to learn* (Rev. ed.). San Francisco, CA: Jossey-Bass.

Zemke, R., Raines, C., and Filipczak, B. (2013). *Generations at Work: Managing the Clash of Boomers, Gen Xers, and Gen Yers in the Workplace.* AMACOM Div American Mgmt Assn.

CPSIA information can be obtained
at www.ICGtesting.com
Printed in the USA
LVHW04s0213290618
582270LV00002B/137/P